THROUGH THE
VALLEY OF SHADOWS

C000040403

THROUGH THE VALLEY OF SHADOWS

MEREDITH RESCE

Authentic

Copyright © 1999 Meredith Resce

First published in 1999 by Golden Grain Publishing,
PO Box 93, O'Halloran Hill, SA 5158, Australia.
This edition published 2004 by Authentic Media.

08 07 06 05 04   7 6 5 4 3 2 1

Authentic Media, 9 Holdom Avenue, Bletchley, Milton Keynes, MK1 1QR, UK.
and P.O. Box 1047, Waynesboro, GA 30830-2047, USA.

The right of Meredith Resce to be identified as the author
of this work has been asserted by her in accordance
with the Copyright, Designs and Patents Act 1988.

All rights reserved.
No part of this publication may be reproduced or
transmitted in any form or by any means, electronic or
mechanical, including photocopy, recording or any
information storage and retrieval system, without
permission in writing from the publisher.

British Library Cataloguing in Publication Data
A catalogue record for this book is available from the British Library

1–86024–495–5

Cover design by Daniel Chattaway
Print Management by Adare Carwin
Printed in Denmark by Nørhaven Paperback

To Nick

*A man of faith, action, vision and courage
and who is also my husband.*

Read each of the
'Heart of Green Valley' books

The Manse – Kate has a secret she doesn't want anyone to know, especially the hateful new minister – the man who has taken her father's place. John Laslett has just arrived in Green Valley as the new parish minister, employed by the patron, Lady Vera Wallace.

At first it seems that the grand lady is full of grace and her intention is to see to his every need. However, there is something strange about the housekeeper she has sent. Kathryn is efficient in every detail, but John cannot seem to break through the cold exterior.

Something is wrong, he is sure, but he doesn't know what ...

Green Valley – Emily Wallace has been given a choice. Either she marries the elderly widower, as her father has asked, or she will be sent from England to live with her aunt.

Even with the tales of wild animals and convicts, Emily chooses to sail to Australia. She simply cannot marry the cruel and arrogant Lord.

Colin Shore has never met anyone so beautiful before. The moment he first saw Lady Emily Wallace at the dock he fell in love with her. But he would never presume that she would be a part of his life.

After all, she was a Lady and he was only a farmer ...

ABOUT THE AUTHOR

Meredith Resce was born and raised in the Southern Flinders Ranges, South Australia, in the community of Melrose.

Meredith and her husband, Nick, have worked in the ministry for eighteen years, having served a six-year period in Geelong, Victoria. They now work with Southside Christian Church in Adelaide, South Australia.

Meredith has completed a Bible College Certificate Course and also a certificate course in psychology. Apart from writing, Meredith Resce lectures to groups on subjects relevant to the development of relationship skills and growth towards emotional health.

She has three children, Elisa, David and Michael.

CHAPTER 1

Green Valley, Rural Victoria, Australia 1891

It was such a shock. One day he was alive, the next he was gone, as quickly as that.

Christine stood with her family in the tiny kitchen, stunned and unable to think clearly. She looked at her sister, Julianne, desperately wanting to ask her what had happened but even as she opened her mouth ready to voice her question, she knew she should wait for her mother's more experienced way of doing things. Ever since they had received word of Pete's death, after rushing with the family to the farm, Christine had rehearsed the question over and over in her mind. Of course she had tormented her mother, Rose Shore, with question after question before they had arrived at the farm.

'But how could it have happened?' she had asked. 'Surely there is some mistake! Pete is only twenty-four years old. He couldn't be dead!'

In the end, Rose had become impatient with her second daughter. 'Please, Christine,' she had answered with a frustrated edge to her tone, 'I don't know what happened. I haven't got any answers for you. We will just have to wait until we get there.'

But even when they arrived, there was nothing to satisfy any of Christine's confusion. Rose had gently probed for answers, but Julianne was too distraught. And when Christine could not tolerate the frustration any longer, and had fired the same question with less tact, she had been quickly reprimanded by her mother.

'Christine!' Rose had forced through clenched teeth. 'Now is not the time. Go outside and bring me in some water.'

As Christine left the tension in the cabin, she knew that the 'water' errand had merely been a reason to get rid of her. She walked away from the front veranda towards the water pump, and began to discipline her own whirling thoughts. She realised that her childish demand for instant answers was selfish, and yet the shock of what had happened just didn't seem real. She still found it hard to believe that anything had happened to her brother-in-law. Besides, where was he now? She hadn't seen him, dead or alive. Oh, how she wanted to relieve her growing alarm as it ate away at her peace of mind.

As Christine worked the handle of the pump up and down, each physical effort brought with it another reason to wonder. 'It can't be true,' she kept saying to herself, in rhythm with the gushing water. 'I can't see how it could be true.'

Soon enough, the bucket was full, and, still tied up in knots of anxiety, Christine began to lug it back across the yard. As she reached the corner of the house, she came face to face with Jack Browning, Pete's younger brother. It only took one look at the agony on Jack's normally smiling face for Christine to know that denying Pete's death was only prolonging the inevitable. A cold dread began to make her stomach crawl as she saw the reality of the tragedy etched into Jack's features. At first, neither one was able to formulate a greeting over and above their individual pain. Christine looked full into Jack's dark, brown eyes, obviously flashing with hurt and anger, and yet she did not fully comprehend the depth of emotion that would have been apparent to anyone else. Nor did

Jack Browning recognise the rising despair that was shimmering in Christine's blue-grey eyes. The pair stared, almost unseeing, for the best part of a minute before Jack tore his gaze away.

'How did it happen, Jack?' Christine forced the question out of her dry throat. She watched, expecting the tall young man to turn back to her with some explanation, but he didn't. Instead, she heard a mild oath escape from his lips, and he began to walk quickly away from her.

'Jack!' She called after him. 'I just want to know what on earth has happened here.' A sob rose in her throat as reality seemed to break through her mental fog. 'I just don't understand!' Her voice trailed away as grief rose up like an all consuming wave.

'God! What is going on here? Julianne can't do without him!' Christine gave vent to some of the brewing emotion. 'They have been in love forever, and now, there's the baby coming. It's not fair! Why him? Why Pete?'

But no matter how many times she agonised over the loss, there didn't seem to be any answers from heaven. As each minute passed, the awful truth began to take shape, and the pain that grew with it loomed almost overwhelmingly.

***

Jack had walked away from his encounter with Christine Shore bubbling over with fury. It wasn't that the fair-haired girl had done anything wrong, but her youthful features, so much like her sister's, had reminded him again of what had happened. Julianne Shore had lost her husband, his own brother, and the very thoughts came crashing in like a wave intent upon destruction. He mounted his horse, kicking it mercilessly in the side to urge it to full pace. He wanted to escape. He wanted to get away from all of the trauma that he and his family now faced.

Once the chestnut gelding was stretched out at a full gallop, Jack began to shout out his rage. 'Why him?' he shouted into the biting wind. 'Why Pete? Why not me? God, I hate you! You shouldn't have done this to us.' Jack didn't register his physical actions, or he might have spared a thought for his poor animal. He had hold of the excess reins and was slapping them angrily, back and forth across the horse's withers.

While he had stood with his mother and father, Jack had held his anguish in check. He would never have dared to scream in the face of God if his mother had been near, but as it was, out here, alone on the hillside, Jack could not hold in his pain any longer. The overcast skies themselves seemed ready to weep with him.

'He was my brother, God,' Jack argued, finally allowing tears to mingle with his cries. 'I loved him. You shouldn't have taken him.'

The storm of emotion was violent but short-lived. It didn't take Jack long to vent the worst of his anger, and once the wind was gone from his sails, he wondered at the dreadful accusations he had flung in heaven's direction; but only for a moment. His pain and loss were still too raw for him to retract his wild, reckless accusations and demands. Even a faint echo of his mother's certain censure, had she been privy to the display, was unable to master a growing resentment. Still, at least there were no more words of wrath. Jack had come to an end of his immediate build up of tension, and with it he drew back on his horse's reins. It was only as he did so that he realised just how fast he had been racing, and how tired his mount had become, as evidenced by the foaming lather that had gathered on the animal's neck.

'Poor old Copper.' Jack patted the horse's sweating neck. 'It's not your fault!'

Even these words were a veiled insistence that someone was responsible for the recent tragedy, and that Jack was not going to forgive that someone quickly.

As he turned Copper towards his brother's home, and began the slow walk back, Jack began to think through the situation again. His thoughts concerning a funeral were still too painful to dwell on for long, and Jack moved on past there to thinking of his sister-in-law, Julianne. Jack had not paid much attention to the talk of the coming nephew or niece. Before this, all the talk of the first Browning grandchild had not held any interest for him whatever. He had not seen it either as a wonderful blessing for Pete, or that he was gaining anything that Jack himself should envy for any reason.

Pete had been in love with Julianne Shore for as long as Jack could remember. Though Jack was in awe of his older brother for many reasons, he had never been able to understand Pete's intense relationship, nor his hurry to marry. When the announcement of the expected child had been whispered around the Browning household, Jack had frowned, almost with disgust. He had completely failed to understand Pete's wide grin of pride. And since that time, until this, Jack had hardly given it another thought; but now, with his brother's funeral imminent, Jack was giving careful consideration to Pete's family, and their need. Perhaps for the first time, Jack could picture Julianne in his mind's eye.

She had always been a vibrant, intelligent, young woman, full of energy and completely devoted to Jack's brother. Together, Pete and Julianne had talked and planned their future. Jack recalled the many times that his brother had shared feelings about what he and Julianne had discussed and finally decided upon. Jack had heard many of the plans that Pete and Julianne had made, from family to farming commitments and decisions that were made to ensure financial security. Jack had always known about their deep relationship, but until this moment, he had never given any thought to Julianne as an individual. Now that it was a topic of thought, an intense thought at that, Jack could see that, despite her strength of will and lively spirit, Julianne was only half a person now that Pete was gone. Why, Pete had been close friends with the girl since they were children. Jack could hardly remember a time when there was no Julianne matched with his brother, Pete. Without him, she was like a loose sail canvas, flapping sadly in the breeze, with no mast to tie to. No matter how many admirable character traits she had, without her husband, Jack wondered whether she would be able to function.

Instinctively, Jack knew this was the truth. Julianne and Pete had been a close team, and without him, Julianne would struggle to hold her own, especially when it came to running the farm and bringing up a child.

'There's nothing for it,' Jack muttered under his breath. 'I'll have to take my brother's place!'

Christine had been working quietly, moving about the small kitchen as if she were a ghost not wanting to be seen. She had returned with the bucket of water, not only subdued in her desire to know, but well aware of the sorrow that had engulfed them all. She no longer had the courage to open her mouth to ask anything.

Rose had long since put Julianne to bed. The older woman had not offered to talk to either her second daughter, or the other members of Pete's family who also sat sombrely about the living area. Christine had made and offered the obligatory cup of tea, but no one seemed particularly inclined towards swallowing anything of substance. Some hour later the group was aroused by the arrival of Doctor Michaels, who had travelled the twenty miles from Brinsford. To Christine it seemed like a wasted effort, having him come to inspect the dead body; Pete was gone, there didn't seem any point in having the doctor come. After all, he wouldn't be able to make him rise from the dead, would he? Still, the learned physician was shown into the spare room where the body had been laid, and after a full half hour, he emerged again to face a room full of questioning faces.

'I'm sorry for your loss,' he spoke gently to the two older women, Rose, and Pete's mother, Elizabeth Browning. 'I cannot say for sure,' he began his explanation, 'but I suspect your son suffered a massive stroke.' He paused for just a moment, and though no one had the courage to ask, he knew that they would not have understood. 'A clot of blood has possibly gone to the brain. In many instances, such a thing can cause brain damage. The victim can be left paralysed in some cases, in others, they exist in a coma for a time. In the case of your son, he was taken quickly. I am so sorry.'

At first it was Elizabeth who broke down in a fit of sobbing, and then Rose, who knew the pain of losing someone so close. No one noticed Doctor Michaels as he slipped quietly out of the house. Finally, tragedy had been given a name, and the family were ready to abandon themselves to their grief.

Jack had met the doctor on his way out of the house. He had asked the physician for his professional opinion, and had received the answer without emotion. As soon as he had seen the doctor on his way, Jack returned indoors to join the family. He saw immediately that all, including his mother and father and sister, had been crying, just as he had cried out in the open air. He did not feel equal to the task of being a counsellor for anyone. Everyone seemed able to find comfort in the embrace of one or other of those present.

Jack did notice, however, that Julianne was not sitting with them, and considering his earlier thoughts, he wondered if he should see if she were all right. But no action seemed appropriate at the moment, and so Jack contented himself by sitting in a chair by the table, allowing his tumultuous thoughts to fight each other for attention in his mind.

'Would you like something to drink?' Christine Shore's voice eventually broke through his mental storm.

'No! Thanks.' Jack was not unlike the rest of them in thinking that he would be unable to stomach anything at this time. But he was suddenly aware of how rude he had been earlier on in the afternoon, and he attempted to make amends. 'I'm sorry ...' he began, suddenly realising just how hard it was to talk.

Christine gave his shoulder a knowing squeeze, empathising with the difficulty they were all having in just talking.

'If you would like to go for a walk, I would like to try and talk about what happened.' Jack suddenly seemed intent on this action. Christine nodded in affirmation, and quickly crossed to her mother, to inform her of where she was going.

Once outside, the pair just walked for some way. There didn't seem to be any hope of exchanging words. To Christine, at least, nothing would possibly have been able to make its way over the lump that sat constantly in her throat, and she knew that her mouth would simply quiver and refuse to support any verbal attempt.

For Jack, though, it was different. He kept playing the scene over and over in his mind, just as he had seen it earlier in the morning. Eventually, he remembered the girl who was walking by his side, and recalled her desperate question of some hours before.

'We had been repairing a fence in the far paddock,' Jack's voice cracked at first, and then became clearer. 'It wouldn't have taken us more than another half hour, and we would have been finished, but Pete said that he didn't feel well.

'At first, I was annoyed, because I didn't really want to come back tomorrow to help finish the job, but then I thought about it. Pete has never been one to complain about being sick. In fact, out of all of us, Pete has always been the one to push on, even if he has hurt a leg, or had a headache. For him to have asked to go home should have told me there was something wrong. I should have listened straight away. Maybe if I had ...' Jack brushed angrily at tears that burned his eyes.

'You couldn't have done anything, Jack,' Christine's own voice was shaking badly, and her facial muscles ached with the intensity.

'But I should have known.' He slapped his side with frustration. 'When we did finally get back, Pete just sat on top of the wagon, and didn't move. I called out to him. Told him to hurry up, and said that he'd feel better after a bite to eat. But he still didn't move. Finally I went around to his side of the wagon. I asked him if he was all right, but he just stared straight ahead. I actually yelled at him. Told him to pull himself together, and then it happened.'

Jack stopped, his adam's apple moving fast as he attempted to swallow his emotion. Christine watched him through a film of tears as he forced himself to continue.

'He called out to me. "Jack," he said. "Help me! Get Julianne." I mean, I was scared stiff. So scared. I had never seen Pete so vulnerable, so out of control. And then he just fell from his seat. I was close to him and caught him. Got him down to the ground, and by this time I was screaming out for Julianne to come. She came out of the house so fast. Too fast, I think, for someone in her condition. Still, by the time she got there, it was too late. Pete was dead. Just like that. I tried to talk to him. I shook him. I called out his name. But he didn't respond.' Tears were streaming down Jack's face now. 'I didn't know what to do, Christine. I couldn't do anything to save him. Julianne kept saying to me, "Do something, Jack. Do something." But I couldn't. I didn't know what to do.'

Christine couldn't help the moisture that flowed down her own face. While she felt pain of her own, she had never seen a man so hurting as Jack was at present. Without thinking about what she was doing, she put her arms around him, and encouraged him to let go his anguish, crying on her shoulder. Neither of them knew how much they had done for the other, just by being available to share the burden.

Christine walked slowly away from the graveside, following her family. Her brother, Colin Shore, supported Julianne on the one side, while their mother, Rose, held his sister's other arm. As Christine watched them move slowly in front of her, she had the distinct impression that Julianne would simply have fallen and died on the rough ground where she was, if her brother and mother hadn't been supporting and urging her all the way home.

The Reverend John Laslett had performed the funeral service, and it had been a tense and strained affair. No one present could have missed the difficulty that the minister had speaking the eulogy. Many people had seen John Laslett conduct one funeral or another, but none of them had ever seen him as emotionally wracked as he was this day; so much so that where he would normally have schooled his features, and controlled his feelings, today his face contorted with grief several times during the ceremony. This uncommon display had the effect of permitting the majority of the mourners to express their grief more openly. The dignity and composure expected in British and Australian alike crumbled in an open show of pain and sorrow; something more akin to the way Christine imagined the mourners of Bible times would behave.

And now, as she thought about it, she had to confess that the venting of grief, though somewhat undignified, had made her at least a little lighter on their return journey home.

Though there had been no restrictions concerning where Pete Browning could be laid to rest, the grave site was the only thing that Julianne had been clear about. She had insisted that her husband be buried not far from the house, under the same tree where her father, Charles Shore, had been buried nearly ten years earlier.

Christine entered the small family cabin, the house she had grown up in, which had until recently been the Shore family home. She led the way inside, going straight to the wood stove, and almost automatically moved the kettle forward over the hotplate, before bending to stoke the fire. She was aware that there were many people, most of them family, who'd come back from the funeral to sit with Julianne for a while.

Pete had been the eldest of twelve children, and though his parents had left the four youngest children at home, the other seven were there with their mother and father. Christine's two sisters, Samantha and June, were also there with Rose Shore, mother of all three; however, their youngest brother, Harry, had been left with Lady Wallace, along with Colin and Emily's baby.

Christine helped Pete's sister, Ivy, set out some biscuits and cake, though she was sure that nobody could possibly swallow a bite in this atmosphere. Still, they went through the motions anyway, finding it easier to go along with what was expected than to question the usefulness of the exercise.

Rose Shore had seen Julianne straight to her bed, concerned for the baby, as much as for her. Conversation in the cramped kitchen was subdued and cheerless. Just as Christine had mentally predicted, no one felt like eating, and though the family were almost awkward in such a setting, no one seemed ready to leave. It was as if there were a collective expectation that somebody would come with news that would make everything all right again.

Christine noticed that Jack Browning didn't stay with the group for more than half an hour before he left, quite agitated. She wondered about Pete's brother, and the sudden mood changes. His anger had been quite evident the first day she had stumbled upon him, but later, Jack had been broken and as vulnerable as a small child. Now Christine saw the anger again and it puzzled her.

It wasn't very long after Jack had left that Mr Browning spoke to Rose, and the three parents followed him outside. Christine instinctively knew that there would be a meeting going on to determine what should be done to look after Julianne and the baby, and without considering if she was wanted or not, she quietly slipped out to join them.

'That's crazy, Jack!' Christine saw that her brother, Colin, had joined the discussion, and was expressing his opinion. She drew quietly up to the group, hoping that they would not exclude her.

'It's a noble thought, son,' Clem Browning spoke slowly, 'but I need to understand what has made you come to this conclusion.'

'It's not noble, it's plain ridiculous!' Colin argued, not worrying to be tactful.

'Col,' Rose warned. 'Jack is at least thinking of someone other than himself.'

'Do you mean to say you approve of this idea?' Colin threw at his mother.

'Approve of what idea?' Christine couldn't keep her presence quiet as curiosity got the better of her. But rather than noticing her, and refusing her admittance to the discussion, everyone seemed more intent on studying the issue.

'It's a huge commitment, Jack,' Clem went on, not directly answering Christine. 'It would be a sacrifice on your part. You're only just nineteen now, very young to be taking on such an enormous responsibility. I'm not sure that you wouldn't regret it in the time to come.'

'I've thought about it, Dad,' Jack eventually stated, quite firmly. 'It's the right thing to do.'

'And how do you reach that conclusion?' Colin remained sceptical.

'Look, Col. I'm not going to argue with you on the issue.' Jack became somewhat defensive. 'It's a principle found in the Bible. The Old Testament, I think. If a man died, then his brother was obliged to marry the widow and bring up the children.'

'We don't live in Bible times now, Jack, for goodness' sake!' Colin sounded exasperated.

'Col!' Rose raised her voice. 'Jack's correct in his Bible history. You can't condemn him for that.'

'You mean, you want to marry Julianne?' Christine had just begun to see what the discussion was about, and she couldn't keep the incredulity out of her voice.

'I mean I have decided to be responsible for my brother's family. Naturally that would mean I would have to marry her. Of course!'

'It's too early to be making such a decision, Jack,' Elizabeth Browning finally entered the argument. 'I think your sentiments are fine, son, but such a proposal would be more than Julianne could bear at the moment.'

'I agree with your mother,' Rose nodded, a look of weariness on her face. 'If Julianne were without any support at all, then the matter would be desperate, but as it is, there are plenty of us to look after her until she has gathered some strength, and is ready to face such a prospect.'

Jack seemed neither relieved nor disappointed. In fact, in Christine's observation, he seemed already resolved, determined to go ahead with his plan no matter what any of the rest of the family said.

'Just give it a few weeks, son,' Clem seemed to read his son's mind. 'Give Julianne some time, and see if you still feel this sense of obligation then. Things might appear different once the baby is born.'

'So what plan do you all have for the immediate future?' Jack sounded cross with them all. 'She can't stay out here on the farm all alone, and she certainly can't be looking after the stock in her condition.'

'I'll look after the stock,' Colin was quick to offer, as if this was a foregone conclusion. 'You don't have to worry about that.'

'As if you don't have enough land of your own to see to!' There was a definite trace of bitterness in Jack's tone as he threw this comment at his neighbour. Once, not so long ago, this house and struggling farm had been all that Colin Shore had owned and was responsible for. Now, as beneficiary to Lady Wallace's large estate and fortune, Colin found himself with more wealth and land than he knew what to do with. It was only at such times as this, when he heard open resentment from his former neighbour, that he realised how different his situation in life had become, and how much this put distance between himself and the other small land-holders.

'I don't intend to repossess the farm, Jack,' Colin's tone softened. 'I gave it to Pete, and now it is Julianne's to do with as she wants. It's just that I am as concerned for my sister as any of you, and I don't mind helping out with the work until she has made permanent arrange-ments.'

Jack looked as if he were about to flare up again, but his father forestalled this by placing a hand on his troubled son's shoulder. 'We can all pitch in with the farm chores,' Clem stated firmly. 'There's no need for any one of us to be misjudging the other's motives.'

'I'd be happy to stay on with Julianne for as long as she needs me,' Christine spoke into the exchange with confidence. 'Perhaps Ivy might want to pop in now and again as well.'

'I think that you two girls will be quite capable of taking care of Julianne,' Rose sounded as if she wanted to make the arrangements and avoid any more friction. 'Are you happy with that, Clem, Elizabeth?'

The elder Brownings nodded their heads in agreement, apparently as anxious to settle the matter as Rose.

'Well, you may all be happy with three young women out here all alone,' Jack was determined to find fault, 'but I'm not! What if something goes wrong in the middle of the night? What if they're attacked?'

'Jack!' Colin sounded exasperated. 'Who ever has been attacked in the night, way out here?'

'The story I heard was that your own wife was set upon by some mad Englishman,' Jack's tone was somewhat smug.

Colin reacted, recalling the incident instantly. There had been a time, several years ago, when his wife, Emily, had become the target of a violent attack. It had been a frightening event and he himself had paid a high price for becoming mixed up in it, trying to protect her. 'What do you suggest then?' Colin asked Jack, wanting to forget the past incident as quickly as possible.

'If Ivy and Christine are going to stay in the house with Julianne, then I will sleep in the hay shed at night, just in case anyone needs me.'

There didn't seem to be any more reason to discuss or argue. For the time being, until Julianne was well and able to think clearly, Pete's brother and sister, and her own sister, Christine, would stay on at the farm to make sure that everything ran as normally as was possible, considering the circumstances.

CHAPTER 2

*C*hristine was frustrated. She had been staying at the farm with her sister for nearly a month now, yet still there had been no improvement in Julianne's condition.

It wasn't that anybody expected her to gain any physical strength, not until the baby was born; it was more her mental state that worried Christine. They had all expected her to grieve, and no one questioned that, but to all who saw her, it seemed that Julianne had given up on life. It was as if she had no wish to gain strength.

'It won't be long until the baby arrives,' Rose tried to reassure Ivy and Christine one day after a visit. 'Perhaps she will show more interest when she has a little one to care for.'

Christine knew her mother well enough to read behind the positive words. Her mother was as concerned as she was.

Half in fear, half in anger, Christine confronted her sister one day. 'You can't just give up like this,' Christine launched into her lecture. 'You're going to have to get over Pete sooner or later, Julianne.' It sounded cruel, and Christine knew it, but it was all she could think of to shock her sister out of her apathy.

'I don't want to get over him,' Julianne spoke quietly, her pale face a mask of misery.

'But what about the baby?' Christine argued. 'It's Pete's

son, or daughter, you know. He would want you to love it as much as you loved him, wouldn't he?'

'I can't do it without him!' Julianne spoke without a trace of her accustomed energy. It didn't seem to matter how much Christine tried to provoke her into an emotional response, Julianne lay listless and quiet. Julianne, who had been so ready to fight and argue with her siblings all through her youth.

Christine had given up on her efforts to stir her sister emotionally for the day, and had escaped outside. She felt a need to be away from the sensitive Ivy, to shake off her own build up of frustration, as well as to take a break from the tension surrounding her sister.

She was no sooner outside than a deep rumble of pent-up feeling, which seemed to well up from the depths of her soul, rose to her throat and eventually tumbled from her mouth. She allowed warm tears to trickle down her cheeks, in marked contrast to the groan of emotion that erupted almost involuntarily, from the depths of her pain.

'Is everything all right?' Christine was startled to hear Jack ask the question. She had not been aware that he was watching her progression from the veranda, and she realised now that he obviously would have seen her intense display of helpless despair.

'Yes and no,' she replied cryptically, wishing that he had not seen her.

'Is Julianne all right?' Jack persisted, himself on edge. 'Is it time for the baby?'

'Not yet!' Christine answered. 'It won't be long though, I expect.'

'Why the tears?'

Christine paused a moment, apprehensive about sharing her deepest fears, but then she thought she detected a trace of compassion in his tone. This inspired a moment's confidence, though she was reluctant to be sure.

Jack Browning had been angry and difficult to get along with ever since his brother had passed away, and there had been times when Christine had become thoroughly annoyed with him and his seeming lack of sensitivity. But now, as she chanced a glance at his face, she was surprised to see his brows knit with concern, and anxiety evident in his dark eyes.

'I don't know what to do with her,' Christine finally confessed, deciding to take a gamble on finding some sympathy in this hard-to-read young man.

'What do you mean?' He did sound alarmed, at least, and Christine's hope of finding an understanding ally rose.

'I don't really know, Jack,' Christine wanted to cry more than ever now, 'I don't think she wants to live.' Two more tears finally broke their bounds and spilled over, and she wiped hurriedly at them.

With all the grief and tension of having lost his brother, Jack had been unusually antagonistic and at times angry. But seeing Christine's open display of fear and anxiety, his normal compassion rose to the surface. He reached out a comforting arm to his brother's sister-in-law, and pulled her close to himself. As he was several inches taller, Christine seemed to fit perfectly under his arm, and she found herself melting into his embrace, and drawing comfort from him. The simple exchange stirred in her an unfamiliar sense of belonging, which she was almost unwilling to give up.

'Julianne is probably just grieving.' Jack spoke in a consoling tone. 'Once the baby is born, she'll get back to normal.'

'I don't think so, Jack.' Christine's voice gave way to shaking sobs as she finally spoke her worst fears; thoughts that had been haunting her for days now. 'I think she's dying, and she wants to die. I don't think she has any thought to get better at all.'

At first Jack was concerned for her. 'You're just tired, Christine.' His tone showed a deep feeling, and he increased the pressure of his arm about her shoulders. 'We have all been through a terrible lot these last few weeks. It will take some time, but Julianne will be all right.'

Christine calmed somewhat, and gradually pulled away, wiping at the corner of her red eyes. 'Do you really think so?' She felt a little better having heard him refute her fears.

'I think that Julianne is probably as scared of the future as any of us. After all, she thinks she is going to have to face it alone.'

'Not alone,' Christine contradicted. 'We will always be there for her and the baby.'

'Yes, but maybe she needs to know that I intend to take on that responsibility. I should have spoken to her before,' he uttered as if berating himself.

'You're not still serious about that?' Christine was suddenly drawn out of her own self-pity and pulled back from Jack.

'She must be worried about how she will take care of the child, and the farm. I should have let her know that I'm prepared to marry her.'

'No!' Christine objected instantly. 'That's not it, Jack. You don't understand.'

'Of course I understand,' he maintained. 'Without a sense of future, of security, of course she is going to feel hopeless. I should have proposed to her when I first said I was going to.'

'Jack!' Christine was now following him across the yard, as he had set out with obvious intent to set the matter right. 'Don't do this, please,' she pleaded. 'It's not you she wants. It's Pete. All she wants is Pete!'

'She needs to know that her future is secure,' Jack threw back over his shoulder.

Christine gathered her long grey skirt and broke into a run to keep up with his long strides. Coming along side of him, she grabbed his well-muscled arm. 'Please, Jack. Listen to me.' Christine knew that Jack could have shrugged her off easily, but he chose to stop and take a moment to search her troubled eyes once more.

'Let me talk to her first,' Christine appealed to him, suddenly shaken by his intense gaze. 'I will tell her about your concern, and your idea.'

'It's not just an idea, Christine,' Jack returned with conviction. 'I intend to marry my brother's widow. I feel strongly that it is my duty.'

'I don't understand why.' Christine sounded confused. 'Why should you feel that it's your duty?'

'I just do,' Jack shrugged. 'Besides it says in the Bible ...'

'I know what it says in the Bible, Jack,' Christine cut him off. 'But I still can't see that it should be reason enough for you to take such a drastic step.'

'It's my decision,' Jack turned back towards the house again, unwilling to justify himself any further. 'If you won't talk to her, then I will.'

'I will tell her about your feelings. I promise.' Christine hurried after him. 'I just don't think that it would be good for you to ... you know ... just blurt it out. I really don't know how she would take it.'

'I think she would be relieved, and you would find that she will improve after that.'

Christine turned from Jack and began to make her way up the veranda steps.

Jack watched her trim figure as she mounted the steps and disappeared indoors.

'Besides,' he muttered to himself, 'you don't understand, Christine Shore. I should have done something to save my brother, and I didn't. I just let him die right before my eyes.'

Christine felt as if she were talking to herself, though she knew full well that her sister was awake, and she was also aware that Jack lurked just outside the bedroom door, listening to the way she would represent him.

'Do you understand what I'm saying?' Christine pressed. 'I know Jack is a couple of years younger than you, but I believe he will be every bit as responsible as Pete was.'

It was as if the mention of her husband's name caused Julianne to recoil in pain.

'I'm sorry, Jules,' Christine noticed and apologised. 'It's just that what Jack says is true. You will have support and provision if he marries you. You won't have to worry about the future.'

Julianne didn't seem to want to respond, and only lay on her pillow, her face turned away towards the wall.

'Please,' Christine pleaded. 'Jack is outside now, listening to this conversation. You should at least acknowledge that you've understood.'

After several more tense moments, Julianne sighed and without turning to look at her sister, she spoke. 'Tell Jack, thank you for caring, but I won't be around for him to worry about much longer.'

'Julianne! Why are you doing this?' Christine cried out, angry. 'Pete is gone, but there are still the rest of us. Don't you care about your baby? About your family?' It didn't matter that Christine was on the verge of hysteria. Julianne simply closed her eyes as if such an action could shut out the unwanted questions and advice. Christine was about to launch into another effort to make her understand when she felt a firm hand on her shoulder. She stopped and looked frantically into Jack's face, amazed to see that his normal look of aggravation was replaced with care and compassion. 'It'll be all right.' He spoke softly. 'Julianne knows that I am here for her. When she's ready, she will let us know.'

Christine opened her mouth to argue, but Jack gently put his finger to her lips, shaking his head in a gesture that spoke of authority, that indicated there was no more to be said for the time being.

Christine walked out of the bedroom upset and indignant. She knew that Jack had followed her, and only waited for him to shut the bedroom door before she began to vent her feelings.

'She won't ever be ready, Jack. Can't you see that? She wants to die!'

'Perhaps when the baby ...'

'No! Not then! Not ever! She has made up her mind, and if I can't make her understand, I doubt that her younger brother-in-law is going to make any difference.'

'She will come around sooner or later.' Jack made a desperate attempt to hide the doubt in his tone.

'I wish you were right,' Christine's eyes welled up with tears again, and she covered her face with her hands in anguish.

Jack quietly left the house. He couldn't find any courage to reassure Christine any more, mainly because he was beginning to believe that she was right, and that thought was frightening in all of its implications. He avoided his sister, Ivy, as she called to him from the garden. He wanted to escape the possibilities that existed in this tragedy-plagued household.

The night had been long and strained with unidentified fears. It had been somewhere about midnight that Christine had woken Jack in the hay shed, and told him to ride over to fetch her mother.

'Julianne's in labour,' she explained, as Jack sat up in his bed of straw. 'I don't like what's happening, Jack,' she confessed. 'It's not good at all.'

Jack had wasted no time in dressing and setting out in the cold, dark night. It was an errand he had been expecting to run for some time, but Christine's dread, obvious in her parting comments, had shaken his own confidence for a happy ending.

Christine had sat with her mother for hours, before changing places with Ivy. The two younger girls would have been awe-struck by the birthing process, had not the circumstances been so grim. Christine should have taken the opportunity to lie down and rest, but she couldn't allow herself the luxury. She was afraid of what the night would produce. Over and over she told herself that when morning came there would be a new little life to celebrate, and yet that dull fear haunted her, never far from her conscious thoughts, and it took every ounce of her willpower to keep focused on the hopeful.

Finally, about seven o'clock in the morning, Rose entered the kitchen from the bedroom, her face pale and drawn. Christine had neither the words nor the courage to ask for news.

'The first one has arrived,' Rose spoke with just a flicker of joy. 'It's a boy.'

'Is he …' Christine wanted to ask the question but was too afraid.

'He's alive and healthy. The second one will be here any moment.'

'The second one?' Here was a thought Christine had not considered before.

'I have suspected there were twins for some time now,' Rose sighed despondently. 'Perhaps this will be the thing that will pull our Julianne through.'

Christine followed her mother back to the bedroom. Perhaps there was hope. Just maybe they would all be able to celebrate yet.

As Christine walked into the dimly lit bedroom, she could see Ivy holding a carefully wrapped baby, tears streaming down her face as she rocked her new nephew. Christine watched as her mother continued to coach and assist as Julianne went through the final motions of delivering the second child. They were all crying now, as the baby girl slid into her grandmother's waiting arms. Christine's hands were shaking as much as her mother's as she held out the clean linen cloth to receive the new-born infant.

'It's a girl, Julianne,' Rose forced the words out over her emotion, wishing more than expecting her daughter to acknowledge.

Christine watched, also hopeful that her sister might miraculously open her eyes, and ask to see the babies. For a moment, all three women held their breath as Julianne did turn her pain filled eyes to her mother. But even though she appeared to mouth some words, nothing was heard, and then she closed her eyes again. Christine was not sure, but she was almost certain that her sister had mouthed the words, 'I'm sorry'.

'Julianne! No!' Christine allowed her voice to rise with her intensity of panic as she interpreted what she thought her sister meant. 'Don't do this to us,' she cried, moving forward. 'Look at her, Julianne,' Christine insisted as she knelt down next to the bed and held the new-born out to her mother. 'This is your daughter. And your son.' She turned and indicated with her hand towards Ivy and the other baby. 'I know you want to die, Julianne. I know you want to be with Pete, but we need you. Can't you see that?' Tears were running down Christine's face, but she was angry. 'Look at me!' she demanded. 'Julianne! Answer me!'

Christine felt her mother's hand on her shoulder, and knew that she was trying to calm her.

'No, Mum!' Christine shrugged her mother's hand away. 'I won't let her go. We need her. The children need her.'

Just as she was beginning to give up hope, Christine saw her sister open her eyes.

'You can do it, Jules,' she encouraged. 'I know you can. Come on. We will all help you.'

'I can't!' Julianne's answer was feeble and her features contorted with pain and sorrow. 'I just can't do it.'

Almost immediately, Julianne seemed to lapse into a state of unconsciousness. Christine saw this as well as her mother, but she still wasn't ready to let go.

'You can, Julianne,' she cried, the tears running unchecked now. 'You can do it.'

Rose watched, wanting above all else that Christine's efforts would produce a miracle. She held her breath praying that Julianne would respond to the desperate plea from her sister, but minutes passed and Rose could see that the effort had been in vain. She allowed a little time before letting her eldest daughter go in her own heart, and when Julianne let go of a last heavy sigh, she knew that it was over. Julianne had done as they'd all feared. She had simply used the extra physical strain and trauma of childbirth as a way to make her own exit from a painful existence she could no longer face. She had died, leaving her children in her family's care, and had gone to join her husband.

When Rose knelt down next to the bed and allowed her grief to rise in waves of sobbing, Christine knew then that there was nothing left to hope for. She clung to the child, her eyes wide, her throat tight and her mind numb.

CHAPTER 3

❧❀❧

No one had really had a chance to recover from the shock of Pete's death, nor the following grief, and so Julianne's passing, though not such a surprise, was merely a continuation of mourning. More than one person, offering condolences, expressed their pity for the two baby orphans.

''Tis a shame,' Mrs Hodges clucked as she inspected the pair. 'No one should have to start their lives in this tragic way. Poor little mites.'

There was little argument from either side of the family as to what the two children should be called. It was hardly discussed before everyone naturally called them Pete and Julianne.

'In remembrance of their dear folks,' Mrs Hodges expressed it nicely for them all.

But though there had been an absence of conflict when naming the babies, difficulties soon arose about the guardianship issue.

Once again, Rose saw the underlying prejudice that had always existed between those with plenty and those without. It was hard to realise that the simple matter of inheritance had put a wedge between her family and those others who had always called themselves close friends and neighbours. To her surprise, even Clem Browning expressed his feelings.

'Just because you folks have all that money, and a grand house doesn't mean that these little ones wouldn't do just as well with us. Money isn't everything,' he stated firmly. 'I've had twelve of my own, and we wouldn't trade the love and closeness we've always shared for all the land in Victoria.'

'But we've always had love and closeness too,' Rose argued, hurt by the comment.

'It's plain enough, Clem,' Colin threw in, annoyed at the objections. 'We have room, you don't.'

'Well, I don't think Pete would want his children growing up spoiled and lazy,' Jack spoke vehemently.

'I don't think he'd want them to starve either,' Colin growled back.

Rose was disturbed as the argument went back and forth. She didn't want this to develop into a fight which would ruin the friendship the two families had once shared, especially now that they shared the same grandchildren.

'I think we should stop this now.' She had to raise her voice to be heard over the two young men shouting at each other. 'If Reverend Laslett were here, I'm sure he would counsel us to pray about the situation for a time.'

'And in the meantime?' Clem asked, quieted but not calmed.

'Ivy and I can stay on here at their farm,' Christine offered her opinion. 'And Jack too, of course.' She threw this in before he could come up with the same objections he'd had before the babies were born.

'Do you think you girls know how to look after a baby?' Elizabeth expressed her doubt.

'I know as much as Julianne would have known,' Christine defended. 'She hadn't had children before either, and if things had been different, she would have been out here with only Pete to help her.'

'Yes, yes,' Clem, choked with emotion, cleared his throat. 'It seems like a sensible solution for the time being.'

'You and I can visit frequently,' Rose addressed Elizabeth. 'I'm sure that the girls will send Jack to us for help if it's needed.'

'Yes.' Elizabeth merely nodded her head with the one word answer, unable to overcome the emotion she felt at having heard her eldest son and daughter-in-law talked about.

But if anyone thought that the situation could be so easily resolved they were to be sadly disappointed. At first, the two girls were able to deal quickly with their sorrow by having so much demand put upon their time. The little girl quickly proved that she would take after her mother in temperament, and meant to indicate her displeasure at every turn. Poor Ivy, who, like her departed brother, had a more placid nature, found that the continual cries for attention and the difficulty in satisfying her needs was a strain almost too much to bear. Christine, who'd fought with her older brother and sister most of her life, had less trouble in coping, but even so, motherhood was a job that neither girl had been prepared for.

Ivy at seventeen had been approached by a young man and her family had expected that an offer of marriage would not be long in coming, but still, to have two tiny lives thrust upon a woman of any age was sure to be a major adjustment.

'I hope we can find some suitable solution soon,' Christine confessed her frustration to Emily during one of her sister-in-law's visits.

'My Charles has been trial enough on my nerves,' Emily admitted. 'I can just imagine how difficult it would be with two to tend to.'

'I'm almost ready to call in the experienced grand-mothers,' Christine allowed a tense laugh. 'Can you imagine how much it has taken for me to own up to my weakness?'

'Are they really that much trouble?' Emily suddenly wondered.

'Pete is not nearly as bad as Julianne,' Christine spoke quickly. 'It's ironic, isn't it? They seem to be almost copies of their parents.'

'Well, I know that your mother would welcome them home with us. If only Mr and Mrs Browning wouldn't feel so offended at the suggestion.'

'And Jack!' Christine added in a disgusted tone.

'Jack?' Emily asked, surprised.

'He's been impossible.' Christine got up from the table and collected the teacups to take to the sideboard. 'He's always insisting that we are not doing the job properly, as if he would know.'

'He does have a lot of younger brothers and sisters,' Emily came quickly to Jack's defence.

'So does Ivy. So do I, if it comes to that.' Christine was not placated. 'It's almost as if he thinks he's the father or something. He's always ordering us about.'

'Ivy doesn't seem to mind, I take it.'

'I think Ivy will be taking up that offer of marriage just as soon as it comes. I don't think she anticipated just how difficult this would be, any more than I did.'

'Well, you have an offer to jump at as well, you know,' Emily gave a knowing smile.

'Offer? What offer? I haven't seen any young men about ready to court.'

'Not marriage,' Emily laughed. 'Remember your wild anticipation to go on an adventure.'

'You mean when we were all set to sail to England and my selfish brother came and spoiled all our plans.'

'All your plans, Christine,' Emily contradicted. 'If you remember correctly, I had no wish to leave this country. It was the last thing I really wanted to do.'

'Thank you very much!' Christine feigned offence.

'Oh, stop it!' Emily laughed. 'You know how totally heartsick I was at having to leave, thinking that Colin didn't love me. You know that I was only going because I couldn't bear to be in the same country as him and not being able to love him freely.'

'I know!' Christine allowed with a warm smile. 'And I am glad that he stopped us in time.'

Emily gave her sister-in-law's hand a loving squeeze.

'You have been the best thing for Colin,' Christine admitted, almost by way of compliment. 'He is a different man now that he's married and settled.'

'And I'm a different woman,' Emily confessed. 'And now we both feel that it is time to take that trip that we almost made those years ago.'

'So you're both going, then?' Christine asked wistfully. 'What about Lady Vera's estate?'

'Colin thinks that Aunt Vera's estate is well under control with the workmen in place, and I think that Charles is old enough to travel now. We have decided that we will be leaving for England just as soon as you are ready to come with us.'

'Really?' All of Christine's heaviness disappeared in an instant. 'Do you mean that you still want me to come along with you?'

'Of course!' Emily grinned, pleased to see her sister-in-law's reaction. 'I know how disappointed you were when I decided to stay and marry your brother. I wouldn't dream of going off and leaving you now.'

'Oh, this is wonderful, Emily,' Christine spoke excitedly. 'Things have been so depressing and dreary since Pete and Julianne … you know. I was beginning to think that the rest of my life was going to be spent living in the shadow of their deaths.'

'I know.' Emily patted Christine's hand. 'Colin says it is time to start making plans, but we won't be leaving until everything has been settled with the children. You understand?'

'Of course.' Christine nodded. 'How long do you think we will be away?'

'Just as long as it takes to sort out my financial affairs, really. My brother seems determined to be difficult about it, so I don't know how long it will take to engage a lawyer and for him to sort through it all. But to tell you the truth, Christine, I wouldn't be going back at all if it wasn't for Aunt Vera and Colin insisting that I go to claim my rightful inheritance.'

'Is it money that you need?' Christine showed her ignorance by asking.

'Heavens, no!' Emily exclaimed. 'I've told your brother time and time again that I would have been just as happy to live out here as in the finest mansion in all England. All I want is the security of a happy marriage.'

'Why, then? Why go back?'

'I thought you wanted to go.'

'I do,' Christine was quick to affirm. 'I just don't understand about the inheritance and all.'

'You see, my brother, Charles, has inherited the title of earl from our father, and all of his estates, but there was another inheritance that came from my mother's family. It wasn't just money, but also several heirlooms – pieces that my brother would probably just as soon pawn to pay a gambling debt as not. From what I understand, he has already spent the dowry my father had put away for me, but he is not able to use the money from my mother's estate. She left all she was entitled to to me. Charles has been furious about it. Apparently he has got himself into some terrible debt, and I know he would never be able to give up his position or privileges. He is going to try and twist the legalities until he has access to my mother's possessions. Aunt Vera wants us to try and stop him. I

really don't care any more, but I'm going to give it just
this one try.'

'Your brother doesn't sound like a very nice person,'
Christine commented.

'I'm ashamed to admit that he's not.'

'I hope I never meet him then.'

'You will, I'm afraid,' Emily spoke quickly. 'We will be
staying with him when we get to England.'

'With him? What do you mean? I thought you just
said ...'

'Oh, Charles might be unprincipled, and ready to
stab his own sister in the back if necessary, but there is
a reputation to uphold. He knows how to behave like
a gentleman if the need arises. There are still enough
relatives and family friends with influence who will
pressure him to show us hospitality.'

'But do you really want to see him? Even under those
conditions?'

'I don't know, Christine,' Emily sighed. 'There are my
memories of father, my family home, things that I want
to face and deal with. But on the other hand, I would just
as soon stay right here and not even think about Charles
and his disastrous life.'

'Well, I have to say that I'm absolutely dying to take
a trip over the ocean, but I'm not quite so certain about
meeting your important earl brother.'

'Well for the time being, at least, you are the temporary
mother of our nephew and niece,' Emily smiled as one
of the babies started to cry. 'Let's just get over that first
hurdle, shall we?'

'If I'm lucky, maybe Uncle Jack could find himself a
suitable wife and then he can take on that duty he's been
so keen to fulfil.'

Christine didn't know just how prophetic her words were about Jack. Though spoken thoughtlessly and in haste, they were soon to come back and hit her with full force.

Another family meeting had been called. Ivy had received her proposal, and had confessed to her parents that playing at foster mother was more than she was prepared for at present.

'I completely understand how Ivy feels,' Christine spoke about their time with the children. 'I know I'm two years older, but I've found the job difficult as well.'

'I think it's time that we made a decision about permanent guardianship,' Clem seemed to assume authority naturally. 'It can't be good for the children having a change of parents every time something new comes up.'

'I agree,' Jack possessed his father's confidence. 'That's why I've come back to my original decision.'

'What original decision?' Colin asked.

'I said it after Pete died,' Jack spoke clearly, 'and I'm still willing to take on the responsibility.'

'You want to look after two babies on your own?' Christine asked the question, half amazed, half annoyed.

'No! Of course not.' Jack sounded equally annoyed. 'I mean that we should marry and look after the children together.'

'Marry?' Christine almost choked on the word. 'Who are you talking about when you say "we"?'

'You and me, of course.' Jack looked at her as if she was a half-wit, and he was impatient at having to explain it twice. Strangely, none of the others in the gathering had anything to say, and they all waited, watching Christine for her response. Suddenly Christine realised that she was the focus of everyone's attention. The blood rose to her face as she understood that they were awaiting her confirmation of this strange plan. All of a sudden she was overwhelmed with a trapped feeling and she burst out in anger.

'What?' she threw at her brother, then quickly glanced at her mother. 'You can't think that this is a serious proposal?'

'I don't know, honey,' Rose answered. 'I somehow assumed that you and Jack had perhaps talked about this before we arrived.'

'Jack? Talk to me? You have to be joking!' She automatically wiped her damp hands across her apron, unaware of the height of her nervous reaction.

'Christine, I'm sorry I didn't come to you with some romantic courtship,' Jack started to explain. 'I haven't thought about us like that.'

'No! I'm sure you haven't.' Christine's sarcasm was evident.

'It's just that ...' Jack tried to continue, but his father intervened.

'I think perhaps we should adjourn the meeting for a while, don't you?' Clem looked pointedly towards Colin as the head of the other family. 'I think Jack and Christine might need some time alone to talk about a few things.'

'I don't need any time,' Christine burst out frantically.

'It's all right, dear,' Rose tried to calm her down. 'There is plenty of time. We don't need to make a rushed decision.'

Christine was flabbergasted. She could not believe what had just happened, and she now felt powerless to prevent the disintegration of the assembly as one by one, the senior family members got up and made ready to leave.

'Perhaps we will meet next week, and talk over this issue again,' Clem commented as he held the door open for his wife to move through.

'Mum.' Christine caught hold of Rose's arm before she too could disappear. 'You don't think I should accept Jack, do you?' She waited, hoping that Rose would give her a clear answer, but all she saw in her mother's eyes was a mournful hope. Before she could stop it from happening, Christine found herself alone with Jack, with only the sleeping babies as chaperones.

The awkwardness between them was tangible. Christine had never been more angry in her life, not even with one of her own siblings during a fight.

'How could you do that?' She finally managed to let out her feelings. 'How could you humiliate me like that?'

'Humiliate?' Jack didn't sound at all repentant. 'We were talking about the future of the children, Christine. What was best for them, remember?'

'Yes, but to just come out and suggest marriage, as if it were no more significant than a trip to town. What were you thinking?'

'I was thinking about the children, Christine. Who were you thinking about?'

She was stumped by the question, and paused open-mouthed for a few seconds, before stumbling on. 'But marriage,' she offered weakly. 'That is such a permanent commitment. I wasn't thinking along those lines at all.'

'Well, now that you are, what do you think?' Jack did not seem ruffled by the exchange at all.

'Think? About you?'

'No! About marriage. It seems like a good solution for all of our family.'

'But what about us? What about me?' Christine objected.

'What about you?' Jack frowned.

'I don't love you, Jack. It's that simple.'

'I don't love you either, yet,' Jack brushed the objection aside.

'It's crazy.' Christine shook her head in denial. 'I won't do it.'

'I reckon you should think about it some more. I know that you girls have a lot of romantic notions when it comes to courtship and marriage, but in the end it's what is built after the wedding that has any lasting meaning, and in this instance, us getting married could mean so much to the babies.'

'I don't believe you, Jack Browning,' Christine shook her head in disgust. 'I can't believe that romance means nothing to you either. I don't think that even you are that noble; that you could just throw away the chances of a loving marriage.'

'Who says that we might not ever love each other?' Jack sounded quite serious.

'At the moment, I say,' Christine snapped. 'This is a foolish idea, Jack Browning, and I don't like it at all.'

'Just think about it, Christine. For the moment, that's all I ask.'

But if Christine thought that she had any allies in other family members, she was sadly mistaken. None of them seemed able to understand her outrage. No matter where she canvassed for support in her condemnation of the plan, she sensed an underlying hope in them that she would go along with Jack.

'It would be a happy solution for both our families,' Ivy suggested meekly, after one of Christine's tirades.

'Happy for whom?' Christine barked, then retracted when she saw Ivy visibly recoil at her harshness. 'I'm sorry, Ivy,' she apologised. 'I didn't mean to shout at you, it's just that I don't know what else to do. Everybody seems to be celebrating over this ridiculous idea, and I can't think of any way to stop them.'

'Do you think my brother is that bad?' Ivy tried again, in a timid voice.

Christine was stumped for a few moments. She saw that same hope show itself unmistakably on Ivy's face, and for just a split second wondered if she were being overly difficult.

'I can't even answer that question, Ivy,' Christine side-stepped the issue. 'I haven't stopped to think about Jack at all.'

'Well, maybe if you did for just a moment ...' the younger girl suggested hopefully.

'I could, if you wanted. I mean, that's what everyone wants, isn't it?' She pushed a straying wisp of blond hair away from her face, refusing to meet Ivy's gaze. Christine knew that if she looked up she would see that Ivy, too, wanted her to marry Jack.

'I have other plans,' Christine finally came out with the excuse. 'I've always wanted to go to England. Emily and I were on our way several years ago, and my bothersome brother ruined my plans. Just as we were about to board the ship,' she added for emphasis. 'And now Jack comes up with this mad idea. What does he think marriage is about anyway? Doesn't he have any plans to find a girl he loves somewhere?'

'Perhaps he loves you,' Ivy offered.

'Ivy!' Christine sounded irritated. 'Let's keep reality and fantasy apart. No! I think I've made up my mind anyway. Emily and Colin are going to make the journey to England, and they've invited me to join them. I plan to go, and I'm not going to let Jack, or the babies, stop me from doing just that.'

Even though everyone stated clearly that Christine was under no obligation to accept Jack, she could not escape knowing that they all hoped she would. The next family meeting was called and it was Christine who called it. She had planned to announce her decision calmly that she had declined the offer of marriage, and if needed, she was going to explain about her desire to travel abroad. It started out well enough. She was over the difficult part, she thought, after announcing the news of her plans, and sat back to hear what the rest of the meeting would bring up.

'Well, son,' Clem turned the focus over to Jack. 'What are we to do now?'

'You make it sound as if I have been the one who's selfishly turned my back on responsibility,' Jack retorted. 'What can I do on my own?'

'What do you mean, selfishly?' Christine's ire was aroused.

'Just that. A selfish decision to travel when your staying could have been the happy solution for all of us.'

'I don't like the way you've put that,' Christine spoke out determinedly, her voice rising in defence.

'What other way is there to look at it?' Jack threw back at her.

'Stop it! Both of you!' Rose intervened, annoyed that Clem had allowed the accusations to go so far. 'We agreed that neither of you were under any obligation, and we shall stand by that agreement. No more reference shall be made to that option. Is that understood?'

Nobody had seen Rose so worked up in a long time, and so the group calmed down considerably.

'Yes! Yes! You're quite right,' Clem allowed, a little shame-facedly. He had been in agreement with his son, and had therefore withheld the intervention that should have come earlier.

The conversation began again, rather tentatively, especially considering the fact that both Jack and Christine had withdrawn into an offended silence. Several suggestions were put forward and discussed, and though none of them were as suitable as Jack's suggestion, no further reference was made to it.

'Well, I suppose it will have to do,' Jack eventually agreed sullenly. 'Although …' He let the words trail off after a pointed look from Rose.

The family party had agreed that one or other of the grandmothers or aunts would take turns in living at the old Shore farm, and Jack would become the permanent guardian, essentially taking the responsibility for his brother's family, as he'd always maintained he would.

'Perhaps you will marry in the not too distant future,' Elizabeth Browning added, hoping to cheer him.

'I want you to know, Jack,' Rose began to speak, 'I think that you have done a wonderful thing for your brother's memory. It is no small thing that you propose to undertake, and you must be congratulated for your singleness of mind and purpose.'

Christine shrank back away from the group as she heard her mother's praise. No one needed to point out the fact that she had shunned the very same opportunity to serve her own sister's memory.

I want to go to England, she thought stubbornly. *And I don't want to marry Jack Browning just because it's convenient.*

CHAPTER 4

C hristine was quite surprised to find that she missed the two babies. While she had been so tied to the responsibility, and had felt totally run off her feet, she had looked forward to the day of departure with a fierce anticipation.

But two days on the ocean had given her plenty of time to think about the things she had left behind in Green Valley. One thing that she sorely missed was terra firma. The constant rolling and rocking motion of the ship upon the waves had quickly upset her landlubber's equilibrium, and Christine found herself longing to be free of the chronic nausea and headache that came as a result of seasickness. The only consolation she found in feeling so ill was to know that her brother, Colin, was faring far worse than she on his first ocean voyage. Christine found that she could afford a weak smile when she considered the picture of misery that was Colin, confined to his berth, constantly moaning about his troubles.

But many weeks aboard ship eventually gave the staunchest land-dweller some sea-legs. By the time the huge vessel had rounded the Cape of Good Hope, and had passed into the tropics, Christine found that she, with all her family, had settled in to life aboard ship. They had become used to the salty sea air, and the fine, mist-like spray that sometimes dampened their skin if the seas were a little rough. It was now only the dreadful boredom that came with confined living space that plagued both brother and sister. Emily, however, seemed to cope far better. It may have been because she had her little boy to tend to all the time, or it may have been that there was some anticipation of drawing closer and closer to the land of her birth.

'I declare,' Emily spoke sternly to her husband and sister-in-law one day, 'I don't think I've ever heard such a lot of complaining before. I don't know if we will ever be able to return to Australia if I have to put up with all this again!'

This comment struck very close to home with both Colin and Christine. Both were feeling quite homesick, even before they had arrived at their destination, and neither wanted to think that they might never return home.

'I'm sorry, Emily,' Christine was quick to apologise. 'I am an ungrateful wretch, and especially when I consider how I could still be stuck at home looking after babies.'

'Sorry, Em,' Colin added. 'We will try to enjoy this experience, but I have to confess, I feel very exposed way out here, away from everything that is familiar to me.'

'Me too!' Christine smiled a sheepish sort of grin. 'It's funny how dreaming a fantasy can be so much more glamorous than the real adventure.'

'It wasn't so long ago that a voyage like this would have taken six months or more to make,' Emily commented, as if trying to make a point. 'You two need to be thankful that this modern steam ship can make it in less than half that time.'

'Don't lecture us, Emily,' Colin complained, half-heartedly. 'You have done this before, and have faced foreign land before, as well.'

'Yes, and remember, I didn't travel with family, nor did I know a soul at my destination. I was so alone.'

'You must have been quite mad to attempt such a journey alone.' Christine suddenly began to see what sort of fears and trials were involved.

'I was delirious,' Emily stated firmly. 'That trip was the worst thing I had done in my life, but when compared to the alternative my father had given me, there was no choice.'

'Yes, and besides, she found a handsome and loving husband in that wild, unknown land,' Colin threw in with a grin. 'You never know, Christine, perhaps you will find the man of your dreams in England.'

'Oh, I hope not,' Christine shook her head.

'Why ever not?' Emily asked, amused.

'I'm missing Australia far more than I ever thought I would, and even before we get there.'

'Well, at any rate, the real adventure will start when we reach London,' Emily turned her thoughts forward. 'I heard the first mate say that we were only two weeks from home. When we get there, it will be the real test.'

'What do you mean?' Christine asked, puzzled.

'She means that her brother is bound to be difficult. After all, in case you had forgotten, Emily is the daughter of an earl, a Lady in her own right. Don't forget that I am less than nothing in this society.'

'And me?' Christine sounded alarmed.

'You might be able to rise to the position of house-keeper after many years of faithful service.' There was no malice in Emily's voice as she spoke. She only wanted her sister, and friend, to understand just what it was they would be facing once they were on the Wallace property.

The closer they came to England, the more nervous Christine became. Emily had been a part of their family for nearly three years now, and she had grown used to the familiarity they shared. It was only now that Emily had ever spoken of the many expectations and frivolous rules that governed her class. Christine knew that Emily was not trying to lord it over them. She was merely trying to warn them of what they might expect.

'I hope that Charles will accept you both, as my husband and sister-in-law – equal and acceptable. But somehow, I fear that he may not.' Emily didn't sound too hopeful. 'It may be that all of my grim stories may come to nothing. I really hope so. I want my English family and friends to accept you for what you are.'

'And what are we?' Colin asked with a cheeky grin.

'Oh, Colin! Stop it. You know I love you, and you, Christine. If I am ever forced to choose, you know that I would choose you and our home in Green Valley any day.'

Christine felt quite secure in Emily's friendship, and she had no doubt that her brother would let no harm come to any of them. So with only a little effort, she was able to push all the anxious thoughts aside, and the closer they came, the more excited she grew. *Fancy actually setting foot in another country*, she thought to herself. *I never thought that it would ever happen, but by tomorrow night, I will have walked on English soil.*

Jack was tired of constantly facing someone new in the kitchen. If it wasn't his mother, or two of his younger sisters, it was Mrs Shore or her two younger girls. Somehow, this was not what he had imagined when he'd offered to be the guardian of his niece and nephew.

Christine Shore had been gone from the valley for over a month, and Jack was gradually trying to let go of the resentment he felt at her having abandoned the responsibility.

'It could have worked out all right,' he mumbled under his breath again, for the umpteenth time. 'She is a pretty enough girl. I could have grown to love her in time – if ... if only she'd have stayed long enough for me to make her love me!'

But Christine hadn't stayed. She had jumped at the opportunity to travel with her brother and sister-in-law, and had taken with her the most suitable solution to Jack's dilemma.

'I'll need to find a wife,' he grumbled as he hitched up the horse to the wagon. 'I won't ever be able to settle in here, and become a real dad to those kids while there is a different woman in the kitchen every time I come inside.'

Jack had actually been thinking along these lines for some time, and though his family usually worshipped at their own home of a Sunday, he began to think that he might visit the Green Valley Church occasionally. One thing was for certain, no young woman was going to come out to the farm offering to take the position of wife and mother. If he was going to find her, he was going to have to mix with more people in the community. After tying the reins to the brake, Jack went back inside the house to fetch his two sisters and the two babies.

Josie and Charlotte Browning, fourteen and sixteen respectively, had the two babies dressed and wrapped up ready to venture out to church. None of them had been in regular attendance at the Green Valley Church. In fact, Jack could only ever remember having gone there twice, and both times were for a funeral. It wasn't that Clem Browning had brought his family up ignorant in matters of the Christian faith, but rather the poorer families of the valley had not been welcome to attend service until just recently.

Lady Vera Wallace, Emily's aunt, had always exercised an unrelenting control over the congregation and minister. She had not deemed that folks like the Brownings or the Shores were suitable sort of people for her to be associating with, and so had made it quite clear that they were not welcome in her church. And that's what it had been: her church. It was only in the last few years, since the coming of the Reverend John Laslett, that Lady Wallace had found any form of challenge to her conscience on this issue. And even then, she had not relented easily. Emily and Colin had been through a lot before Lady Wallace could see that someone of such 'low' breeding could actually be as much a person of integrity and character as anyone she'd ever met in her exalted circles. It had only been at this point of revelation that Lady Wallace agreed that it was time to open the doors of welcome to the entire population of Green Valley.

Up until this point, Jack's family had not yet gotten used to the idea of going out of the family home for Sunday devotions, and as Jack drove the horse along the dirt road leading into the small town, he felt considerable nervous tension at facing a different routine.

'Welcome, Jack,' John Laslett let his surprise show in his tone. 'It's wonderful to have you and your sisters join with us today.'

Jack took the minister's hand, and felt the sincerity in his grip, but he couldn't find any intelligent words to answer, and so he led his sisters into the aisle, and shuffled into a pew near the back. He noticed near neighbours, Ned and Lilly Miller, and their children, seated across the way from where he had chosen to sit. Giving a quick nod of acknowledgement, Jack then put his head down, uncertain what was expected when attending a church service.

The next hour passed without any breach of etiquette, and Jack found that John Laslett's easy and friendly manner made the sermon agreeable, if not enjoyable. After the congregation had been dismissed, Jack was quickly approached by Rose Shore and her family.

'What a pleasure to see you here,' Rose beamed. 'Let me see my babies.' She immediately turned her attention to her two grandchildren, leaving Jack to gaze around at the rest of the crowd who stood outside the entrance to the church.

Ned Miller approached him and wasted no time engaging him in conversation about farming matters. 'How are things going out at Pete's place?' Ned asked, unaware that the mention of his brother's name caused an arrow of pain to pierce Jack's heart.

'Things are pretty good,' Jack answered in a non-committal way.

'You've put a bit of crop in out near our place, I see,' Ned commented. 'How's it going?'

'Actually, it was Pete's idea to put that crop in,' Jack confessed. 'I guess everything is going along as well as can be expected. Dad is the real expert, you know. He'd know the answers for sure.'

'Well I guess it's your land now, Jack,' Ned went on. 'You're going to have to become your own expert.'

Jack nodded in acknowledgement of the fact.

'How are the two little ones getting along?' Ned seemed determined to have all the information he could get.

'Once again, I'm not the expert,' Jack dodged the question. 'You'd have to ask my mother, or Mrs Shore, over there.' He jerked his head over his shoulder in the direction of Rose and his sisters.

'I admire you, Jack,' Ned admitted. 'To take on those little ones is a really noble thing. If you ever need anybody to talk to about being a dad, other than your own father of course, I'd be happy to share what I know.'

'I hear you're one of the best,' Jack gave a teasing smile. 'Colin Shore quotes you on just about every aspect of fatherhood.'

'Does he?' Ned smiled. 'Colin's a good mate. I've missed him while he's been away. I hope they don't stay away forever.'

With the mention of Colin, the thought of Christine followed, and Jack found himself back to the point of his original purpose.

I need to find a wife, Jack thought, trying to focus on the young girls present at this gathering. *I must find one soon, for the children's sake.*

From the moment Colin led them down the gangway, and her feet touched English soil, Christine was overwhelmed. She had been trying to picture what this new country would be like, ever since they had sailed out of Port Phillip Bay in Australia. Now that land and that culture seemed a lifetime away. For just a moment, Christine felt another wave of homesickness, but she was quickly drawn out of it as the sights and sounds of the wharves at Portsmouth rose up to intrigue her.

Despite the fact that Emily had tried to describe her former homeland, neither Colin nor Christine had imagined anything like the scenery that greeted them. Colin elected to transport the small party by land to London, making use of the relatively new railway lines. Emily had objected, of course. Her childhood had been one of private carriages, and the huge, iron, steam-belching monsters were considered vulgar and beneath her dignity. But there had been subtle changes in England, even during the few years Emily had been away. The attitudes of the

Queen and her husband, Prince Albert, and their family-and-duty-centred existence, gave the lead to the English aristocracy who were also beginning to abandon the scandalous lifestyle of earlier generations. Society was gradually becoming dominated by middle-class values, and so the Shore family were in no way exceptional riding on this new public transport.

Christine marvelled first at the other passengers. They seemed quite proper, despite Emily's fear that they would be beneath them. The ladies' clothing was quite lavish in colour and material, but not at all lacking in modesty. Emily was somewhat gratified to notice this, as not so long ago, the ladies of her acquaintance had been shamefully bold about the exposure of shoulders and bust line. It was a relief to her to see that the normal attire seemed to include large cape-like coats, that were generous in size, covering the greater part of the gowns underneath.

But the study of the English ladies soon gave way to fascination of the breathtaking views that were to be seen through the railway carriage windows. Christine was mesmerised by the passing countryside. She had been born in Green Valley and had made only two trips outside that area. Now in contrast to the thick, untidy Australian bush, Christine saw mile upon mile of rolling green hills, all cleared and neatly divided into fields by dark-green hedges. The land around Green Valley had been laboriously cleared by the pioneers, and in some sections, stone walls had been erected by the convict labour of years gone by, but there were still many acres of virgin scrub. Even on the old Shore property that Pete and Julianne had farmed, there was still only a portion that had been cleared of trees and stumps enough to plant hay crop. Christine was amazed at the different vegetation, the rich green that seemed to be everywhere.

This was supposed to be summer, and yet the grass was thick and rich, unlike the dry, yellow-brown of her own land.

As the train seemed to eat up the miles, Christine took in all the sights of the English villages: the quaint little buildings that sat in clusters, all of them seemingly ancient; many, many brown, stone cottages, usually two or more storeys high, their shingled roofs showing the signs of age and time. The towns in Australia that Christine knew were only new. They wouldn't have been built more than fifty years before, and public buildings such as churches and schools were only just appearing even in her own lifetime. To realise that England was a land of ancient history was a staggering thought, and many questions arose in the young woman's mind.

Still, if the small party from Australia was captivated by the sight of the English countryside, nothing could have prepared them for what they saw on coming into the old city of London.

They had been travelling from the coast the entire day, and the daylight had already begun to fade by the time they arrived in the city. Emily coached her husband on how to order a cab, in the way she had seen it done previously. Christine heard the clip-clopping of the horses' hooves on the cobbled streets as they began to make their way away from the station towards the address Emily had given the driver.

Again Christine began to feel many sensations crowding in on her. Passing through an open square, she didn't quite know what to think as she watched the different people walking past outside. She had difficulty in reconciling the contrast made by the well-dressed woman in a tailored coat and fancy hat, buying a posy from the small, dirty-faced street-urchin, carrying a too large basket of flowers. There was a mounted policeman wearing the shell-domed helmet, calling out now and again to someone in the busy pedestrian traffic across the square.

After only a short time, Christine began to feel dizzy with all of the hurrying and scurrying, and more people than she had seen in her entire life, even in Melbourne.

Finally, Emily spoke the words that they'd all been anticipating.

'We're here!' she sighed. 'Welcome to my London home.'

Christine opened her eyes again, after having had them closed for the last fifteen minutes, to absorb the sight of what she knew was just the London residence of the Wallace family.

It did not have the gardens or trees that Christine had imagined, after the pattern of Lady Vera's home in Green Valley. In fact, it was built quite close to the roadway; a large stone wall, with wrought iron spikes interlaced, separated the residence from the footpath.

Christine could see that there were at least three storeys, each level boasting five large windows, and along the top of the house was a stone balustrade that indicated there might be some access to the flat roof. The architecture was fascinating, and Christine only just heard Emily describing this house as one of the younger homes, built only in the last hundred years or so. To Christine, this dated the house as positively archaic.

The cab had pulled to a standstill now, and Christine was forced to turn her thoughts from the ornate Corinthian pillars that stood either side of the grand doorway to the more disturbing prospect of meeting the revered earl, Charles Wallace.

From the first she'd heard of him, Christine had wished that he was not to be included in this magical visit. When she thought of Emily's account of his behaviour, she didn't like the way he had treated her with such indifference, verging on disdain. And now, just as soon as their trunks had been removed from the back of the horse-drawn cab, and they had all alighted onto the street, they would be moving into this haughty man's domain.

Christine allowed anxiety about this meeting to steal some joy from the celebration of having finally arrived. And the thing was, she could sense that her sister-in-law, Emily, was also troubled about the imminent reunion. She saw her scold the baby over a nonsense issue, one that would not normally have bothered anyone.

'Are you all right?' Colin asked his wife, squeezing her hand as if to give her extra courage. 'Are you ready to face the past?'

'Only because you are with me,' Emily answered quickly. 'If I had not married you, I would sooner have died than come back to be bullied by Charles.'

'I'm feeling much more reassured now.' Christine made this casual comment, before picking up her skirts to follow the party indoors.

However, ten minutes in the Wallace house revealed that all the apprehension about meeting the earl, Charles Wallace, had come to nothing. Emily didn't quite know whether to feel disappointed or relieved to find only the staff to greet them. The housekeeper was professional but distant in her welcome, quite aware that the party was expected, but only willing to offer the perfunctory words necessary.

'Is my brother in town?' Emily asked, annoyance beginning to dispel her confusion.

'No, Madam,' Mrs Stewart answered.

'Are you expecting him anytime soon?' Emily wanted more information, and was becoming angry that this employee did not seem in the least bit concerned with putting her in the picture.

'No, Madam,' was the only answer the large woman seemed willing to give. 'Peters will take your things to your rooms, and I will have the cook prepare tea for you. You may come down in half an hour.'

Emily didn't say anything there, but she was furious. She had never met Mrs Stewart before, nor the silent and stern-looking Peters. Obviously, the staff who had worked for her father were no longer employed by the new earl.

'Well, that was some welcome,' Colin released a breath of tension. 'Has your housekeeper always been so helpful?'

'I am so angry I could burst,' Emily finally let out her feelings once the butler had left the room. 'Who does she think she is, telling us we may come down in half an hour? If my father was alive, she would not dare tell us what we should do.'

'I was beginning to wonder who the authority in the house was,' Colin admitted. 'I know it is different with Aunt Vera, now that my family are basically the staff as well. But I had assumed that it would be different here.'

'Different, yes! But not the staff telling the family what they may and may not do.'

'Don't let it upset you, Em,' Colin drew her into an embrace. 'So long as we have a dry place to stay, and some food to eat, what does it matter?'

Emily wanted to yield to her husband's efforts to calm her, but there were too many things that had changed since she had left.

The last time she had been in this house, her father had been here, in charge and ruling with justice. To walk over the familiar threshold, into the grand house where she had spent many months of her life as a child, only to find her father gone, and the loving, faithful staff replaced with servants who were less than gracious, was a shock. Emily was upset, and she didn't think that even Colin's understanding and gentle words would be enough this time.

Christine had been shown to another part of the house altogether, and it didn't take her long to realise that she had been allotted the room usually reserved for the nanny. She saw the manservant put her young nephew's trunk in the room directly adjacent. There was an adjoining door between her small, and rather bare room, and the nursery right next door.

Christine didn't want to take offence at this obvious slight. It was not Emily's fault that she had been acknowledged only as a travel companion or servant instead of a guest at Wallace House. In fact, Emily had gone out of her way to warn Christine of what she might expect.

Looking around at the scant furnishings, Christine determined not to let this 'welcome' sour her outlook. After all, if they had never met Emily Wallace those years ago, Christine would never have set foot outside Green Valley, let alone travelled all the way across the world.

As soon as Peters had left her alone, Christine began to unpack her own things, hanging up her sensible, practical clothes in the small oak wardrobe. It didn't take long for her to sort out her belongings, and she then moved into the nursery, next door, to unpack baby Charles' small outfits, coats and shoes. Christine had no idea that any normal guest in this house would not even think to lift the lid of their own trunk, let alone sort out their belongings.

When Emily eventually saw the job her sister-in-law had done, she decided to let her outrage die away. Perhaps it was best to allow Christine to function as normal; and here in England that meant that she would be cast in the role of servant.

CHAPTER 5

J ack found himself going over the past few weeks in his mind. He had been rather surprised at just how easy this particular courtship had gone. In all of his imaginings, he had pictured himself being laughed at, rejected and consequently thoroughly humiliated. These fears in themselves had been the cause of many weeks procrastination.

He had seen Eunice Booth the first time he'd ventured out to church, but it had been three weeks before he'd plucked up enough courage even to talk to her. Now, the day he had actually asked her to marry him, Jack found himself amazed, firstly at himself for having made it thus far, and secondly at Eunice for accepting his proposal so happily. If it hadn't been for the stern-faced mother, Jack felt he could have been perfectly happy with himself.

Eunice was not what Jack would have called a classic beauty. She was too tall and too ungainly for that. Her face was pretty enough, he supposed, but even as her image ran through his mind, Jack found himself comparing his new fiancée with the fine, clear complexion and lively blue-grey eyes that had haunted his thoughts for some months now.

He shook his head in an effort to rid himself of the memory of Christine Shore. Eunice was here and openly available while Christine was not.

Despite Eunice's rather plain brown hair and a very unremarkable nose, covered in freckles, Jack found her to be lively and full of mischief. If nothing else, Eunice Booth was always enthusiastic about whatever Jack suggested. Even though Mrs Booth had scolded her a hundred times, Eunice persisted in her flirtatious manner, carelessly throwing her arms about Jack's neck, and kissing him boldly, even in public.

Jack had felt some reserve at her uninhibited expressions of affection; for one thing, he had not wanted to upset his prospective parents-in-law, and so he had officiously lectured Eunice on the rules of propriety and decency. She had merely laughed at his lecture, and brushed it aside.

'Oh! You sound just like Mother!' she scoffed. 'She's always making some fuss about this or that. Let go of yourself, Jack. We're young. We're supposed to have fun!'

'Yes, but I'm not sure that ...'

'That what?' Eunice's face became suddenly serious. 'Don't you think that a love like ours should be expressed without shame?'

'Yes ... no ...' Jack stumbled. 'It's just that it isn't polite to act like that in public.'

'What about now? Now that we are alone?' She seemed to take on the role of an experienced seductress, running her cool hand around the back of his head, down his neck and onto his chest.

'Eunice!' Jack's throat had constricted as he felt a fiery passion rise from within. 'I'm not sure ...'

She wasted no time in silencing him, skilfully covering his mouth with her own, and in so doing chasing away his doubts.

At first, Jack tried to fight her actions, his conscience vaguely uneasy, but as he felt the warmth of desire in her touch, he lost all sense of moral conviction. It wasn't until she pulled away from him, letting out a careless giggle as she did so, that Jack became frightened of his own inability to control his physical urges.

'There now, Mr Jack Browning,' Eunice teased. 'What have you to say about that?'

Jack couldn't think of anything to say at all. The lively young girl had stirred the slumbering male in him, and for once the thought of marriage brought more than a consideration of having a mother for the children.

And Eunice continued on in this manner, every time she got a moment to spend with Jack. Mr Booth had spoken firmly with his daughter and prospective son-in-law several times, a speech which Jack took quite seriously.

'I do not approve of your relationship with my daughter,' he had launched out at Jack one Sunday afternoon. 'It is bad enough that I have been forced to consent to your proposal, but this scandalous behaviour is too much to put up with. Eunice could have done much better than you, young man, and I'm not altogether sure it would not be better to send her away to Melbourne to her aunt. As it is, decent folk are beginning to talk about your carry on. I'm not at all happy with you.'

'I'm sorry, sir.' Jack was mortified by the comments. 'I believe you are right, but Eunice is very hard to discourage.'

'Quite so. And it is only her relentless nagging that has made me give in to you in the first place. I wanted more for her.'

'I'm sorry, sir.' Jack apologised, hanging his head, thoroughly intimidated.

'Yes, well see that you curb your affection.'

There were two things that motivated Jack now. Firstly, he was horrified to think that he had allowed respectable folks to think that he was conducting himself in a manner that was considered in some way loose. That had never been his intention or his heart.

It was true that he had set out to find a wife purely for reasons of convenience. The initial attraction he had had for Eunice was the fact that she was single and of marriageable age. But now, since the young woman had not only been kindling a fire in him, but also fanning it into flame, Jack had become totally hypnotised by everything she did. His second motivation was now fear. He began to dread the thought of not having her. Eunice Booth had Jack where she wanted him.

His own family noticed the change in him. At first his parents had been glad that their son had found something other than responsibility to focus on. They had felt that Jack had become far too serious for a young man of his age, and that the death of his brother had stolen some joy of life from him. So the entrance of Eunice Booth into his life had been, at first, a welcome addition. But now, Elizabeth had commented several times to her husband about the flighty and inattentive behaviour of the girl.

'Do you think I'm just acting like a mother who doesn't want to let go of her son?' she asked Clem during one conversation.

'I don't believe you had this concern when Pete was courting Julianne,' Clem answered gently.

A tear rose to the grieving mother's eyes as she remembered the two young people who'd been so dear to them, and who were now gone.

'Julianne was different,' Elizabeth finally spoke. 'She was lively enough, I know, but there was a different quality about her.'

'Yes!' Clem nodded in agreement. 'She loved and respected our son.'

'Don't you think Eunice loves Jack?' Elizabeth seemed surprised at the thought.

'No, I don't. I think Eunice loves Eunice. I don't think she has ever thought of anyone but Eunice.'

'But what about Jack? Surely he must love her!'

'Why surely?' Clem asked with confidence. 'We both know he intended to find a wife, no matter what. When he proposed to Christine, love was not a consideration. All he could think of was finding a mother for those children.'

'Yes, but now ... I mean they seem to show so much affection for one another.' Elizabeth sounded confused.

'Too much, if you ask me,' Clem divulged his thoughts openly. 'I don't think Jack loves Eunice Booth. I think he is bewitched by her. I haven't heard the boy speak a sensible word since they became engaged.'

'That's how it is, sometimes.' Elizabeth didn't sound confident in her defence. 'Sometimes young people are madly in love when they marry.'

'Elizabeth.' Clem suddenly became tender in his speech. 'I know that ours was an arranged affair. I know that you were just a frightened girl when we married, but we both know what real love is.'

Elizabeth nodded as the tears overflowed her eyes.

'Even Pete and Julianne didn't really know what depth of love a couple can share over a long period like us.' Clem went on. 'They were best friends when they were courting, and then they began to know the depths of true commitment and love ... if only ...' There was a tense pause as they both struggled to regain their composure.

'I don't like what Jack is building here,' he continued, swallowing back his emotion. 'His is not a relationship built on friendship or respect. At the moment, all I can see is a young couple who have become slaves to their physical desires.'

Elizabeth knew it was true, but hearing it spoken out so plainly brought a spasm of pain to her heart. All of a sudden she felt she really *was* one of those mothers who didn't want to let her son go. Not like this, anyway.

The day that the earl, Charles Wallace, arrived at his London house, a cold wind of dark foreboding seemed to blow in with him. Up until then, the Australian visitors had been managing quite well.

Colin had spent quite some time convincing his wife that they could live just as well without a 'royal' welcome and fanfare, and he had begged Emily to accept that he and his sister really felt quite privileged even to be allowed admittance to such a grand mansion.

Emily had struggled with her anger, feeling offended at the deliberate indifference of her brother, and had experienced many conflicting emotions listening to her husband's appeal for contentment. Eventually, she yielded her resentment but only for the sake of peace. To have ranted and demanded the attention she felt was due to her from the staff appeared to be an expenditure of energy not worth the effort.

And so when Charles Wallace marched into the entrance hall, a flurry of various servants in attendance, Christine was astounded to see the resident staff snap to attention, bowing and fawning over the man as if he were the Prince of Wales. She stood at the bottom of the stairs, her mouth agape to see how someone deemed so important could be treated.

A short man with a pale complexion, Emily's brother was not at all the huge giant of a man that Christine had imagined. He wore a fashionable suit of clothes, well tailored and obviously expensive. He sported a red handkerchief in his coat pocket, that matched the tie at his neck, and he had a gold watch on a chain, which he brought out of his waistcoat pocket to take note of the time. He was apparently quite in vogue, though Christine didn't like the way he wore his hair, especially the large bushy sideburns that covered the whole side of his face.

'You there, girl!'

Christine was snatched from her stupor as she realised that the man had addressed her. Having assumed that she was an invisible observer, she was somewhat embarrassed to find him staring furiously at her.

'Haven't you something you're supposed to be doing? Who hired this girl?' He directed his anger towards the housekeeper. 'Mrs Stewart! Why haven't you informed this girl of her duty?'

'I beg your pardon, sir,' the older servant curtsied with deference. 'This girl is with your sister. From Australia, sir.'

'I don't care where she's from,' he snapped, incensed. 'Even my dear sister would require her maids to see to their own business. Get off with you!' He threw the order to Christine, and she didn't have the courage to even address the man, let alone inform him of her slightly raised status of sister-in-law. But just as she was about to turn in flight to her room, Emily's voice cut across the gathering.

'We are very glad to see you, Charles.' Emily's tone belied her words as she was obviously angry. 'I see you have met my dear sister, Miss Christine Shore. She is possibly quite upset at having been barked at so. Perhaps you would care to apologise.'

Emily's voice held more authority than she'd ever dared used with her brother before, but she was absolutely furious at the way he'd spoken to Christine.

'Sister!' Charles burst out. 'What in God's name do you mean?'

'My husband's sister, Christine, and by the way, you might like to be introduced to him. He is down the hall in the library.'

But in fact, Colin was not in the library, but on his way to see what the commotion in the entrance hall was about. He arrived just in time to hear his new brother-in-law spit out a most uncomplimentary remark.

'You could have done better than this, Emily.' He waved his hand derisively in Christine's direction. 'I say, look at the way she's dressed.' Christine was suddenly aware of her plain grey skirt and ordinary work blouse from home. 'Honestly!' Charles went on. 'How was I to know she wasn't your maid?'

Emily wanted to shout and scream at her brother all at once, and possibly would have, had not Colin stepped boldly forward.

'I must offer you our thanks,' he spoke with confidence. 'My wife and sister are most grateful for your hospitality.'

For once, Charles was momentarily intimidated. Being not above five foot six, and slight of build, he found his confidence shaken when having to stare up at a much taller, more athletically-built figure.

The difference between the two was marked. Colin was tanned and fit, having worked many hours of physical labour. Charles felt the strength of the brawny Australian in the handshake offered. He was an English gentleman who typically ate too much rich food, and did practically nothing for himself, so Charles found himself very much diminished in comparison.

But his moment of inferiority didn't last long.

'So, you have come home!' There was no loving welcome in his tone as he addressed Emily; only bored indifference. 'I must say I'm surprised you had the nerve after defying me, when I wanted you to marry Derickson.'

Emily opened her mouth to challenge him, but Colin put a gentle pressure on her arm, and spoke himself.

'Emily has very much wanted to pay her respects to you, for the sake of your father's memory.'

'Yes! And I suppose she also wants to pay respects to my money as well.'

'Money!' Emily could not restrain herself. 'I heard you'd lost most of your money, and have worked your way through my dowry as well.'

'My dear girl!' Charles was all condescension again. 'When I heard you'd chosen some foreign stranger as a marriage alliance, I understood you had relinquished all your ties with our father. After all, the dowry was meant for Derickson, not for some ex-convict who comes from who knows what lineage.'

Emily was ready to burst out again, but once more Colin spoke smoothly and calmly: 'I quite understand your misapprehensions.' Only Christine could hear the amount of self-control he was applying to keep from physically assaulting the man. 'You could not possibly have known the calibre of me or my family, and so we are willing to forgive your not sending us a wedding present.'

'But now that you're here ...' There was obvious cynicism in Charles' tone.

'Now that we're here,' Emily broke her restraint, 'I would very much appreciate being treated as one of the family rather than a group of unrelated beggars.'

'Of course!'

Even though Charles Wallace appeared to be outwardly compliant, Christine could sense that he had no more wish to accommodate Colin or herself, than if they *had* been unrelated beggars. From that moment on, their physical status seemed to improve, yet Christine sensed an underlying resentment from both the earl and his staff alike. From all that she had observed, and from what she'd learned from Emily, Christine was quite content to keep to her part of the house, thus avoiding the arrogant and apparently malicious head of the house.

'How long do you think we will be staying in England?' Christine asked the question one morning, when she was alone with Colin and Emily.

'Are you homesick?' Emily asked her own question in place of the expected answer.

'Would you be offended if I confessed to being a *little* homesick?' Christine asked, tentatively.

'No!' Emily looked sad. 'I'm sorry that you have not seen some of the beauty of England, Christine,' she apologised. 'My father's estate in the country is magnificent. The house is twice the size of this one, and the grounds are vast. If things were not so strained between Charles and me, I would love to have taken you to visit for a few weeks.'

'But that would not be possible as it is,' Colin was quick to throw in. 'We are still haggling through legal procedures with the lawyers, just trying to have the inheritance from Emily's mother made available.'

'It's all right,' Christine tried to sound cheerful. 'I have had some interesting walks about the London parks, and we are not too far from the Thames. Perhaps one day, when you're not too busy, we might even drive by the Queen's castle. What is it called?'

'Windsor Castle!' Emily supplied. 'And I hope that we can hire a chaise and go driving some more,' she sighed. 'I do want you to see something of the country while we are here.'

Christine did not openly talk about a lot of what she felt. She didn't mind taking the role of nanny for her nephew. He was a delightful child at any time. She didn't even mind being left alone to amuse herself with walks and reading.

But now that the earl was in London, Christine was somehow afraid. He carried with him a dark and somewhat frightening presence. Colin and Emily seemed to have many engagements with her lawyers and other friends of influence, which left Christine at a loose end, responsible for her own entertainment. She wouldn't have minded this so much if it didn't mean that there was a likelihood of being left alone with Charles Wallace.

She didn't know what, but there was something about that man that caused Christine to feel very much that she wanted to board the first possible ship home.

Jack walked towards the Booths' home, his stomach churned into knots. He had just come from a conversation with his father where cross words had been exchanged. Clem Browning had decided to become more forthright in his attempts to counsel his now eldest son, and Jack had reacted in an angry manner.

It wasn't that he hadn't heard this sort of advice before, because he had; from the Booths, from the reverend, from his parents and even from Rose Shore. He had heard it all before, and inside he agreed with them, but it was far worse than any of them could have imagined now.

The last time he had been to the Booths' residence, he had gone aware that only Eunice was at home. He had heard that she was staying home from church with a headache and he had excused it in his own mind as concern for his fiancée. But now, as he approached the same garden gate again, he wondered what on earth had possessed his mind. Whereas now he was full of agitation and regret, then his mind had been in a fever, and he admitted to himself that he had almost been looking for this excuse to be alone with the girl that he 'loved'.

'I need to talk with you,' Jack spoke rather sharply to Eunice when she came into the room. 'Would you like to walk a while?'

Eunice didn't seem to be her usual bubbly self, but merely nodded, grabbing her shawl to throw about her shoulders on the way out.

'Well, what has put you in such a temper today?' Eunice began the conversation the moment the pair were out of earshot.

'You know very well,' Jack snapped at her. 'What happened last Sunday was wrong. It was a mistake, and now we are going to have to fix it up.'

'Oh, fiddle-faddle. What's done is done. There isn't any call to be getting all gloomy about it.'

'I'm not going to argue with you, Eunice.' Jack was in a temper, not just because of the moment, but also because of the way he had spoken to his father just recently. 'I've decided that we will get married just as soon as Reverend Laslett can arrange it. Hopefully next week.'

'Next week!' Eunice's response was swift and fierce. 'I'm not going to up and marry you just like that!'

'We have no choice, now,' Jack argued. 'We have done the wrong thing, and now we must make it right.'

'You have done the wrong thing, Jack Browning,' Eunice huffed. 'I'm not going to wear any blame for last Sunday. If anybody asked me, I would tell them that you took advantage of me.'

'Advantage!' Jack exclaimed, his ire raised. 'Eunice, you have been flirting with me ever since you met me, and that's not all.'

'It's not my fault if you can't control your passions,' she made her excuse. 'Anyway, I have no intention of being dragged out to that little run down shack and being made permanent house maid for some dead person's brats.'

Jack surprised even himself when he turned on his companion and took her by the shoulders, shaking her violently as he spoke. 'Don't you ever, ever speak about my children like that.' A spark of fury flashed in his eyes, and for a moment she was stunned by his performance. But when he let go, realising just how hard he was shaking her, she regained some composure.

'I do beg your pardon, sir,' she apologised sarcastically. 'I have trodden on sacred ground, so it would seem.'

'Look, I'm sorry, Eunice,' Jack yielded to the urge to plead. 'I didn't mean to hurt you. I love you, and I want us to be properly married.'

'I'm not ready to be married yet,' she remained obstinate.

'We must,' he pursued.

'Why must we? What is the hurry?'

Jack spoke quietly, afraid to broach such a delicate subject. 'You could be with child. My child!'

For once, Eunice was without words, and Jack noticed that her face had paled considerably. Eunice had been brazen and flirtatious, and even seductive. She had loved the feeling of being able to lead Jack on. But she had never talked with anyone about having relations with a man. She had not cared that everyone thought it was wrong, but then she hadn't realised that anything serious could result from it.

'What do you mean?' She eventually asked the question, a fear now apparent.

'Eunice Booth. Hasn't your mother told you anything?'

'No! Not about that. Why should she?'

'Because we are to be married.' Jack held a patient note in his voice considering the tension that existed.

'Yes, but not yet.' Eunice mumbled a few words, then:

'You don't mean to tell me that I could be … that what we did …'

'I thought you would have known that.'

'Are you sure?'

'No! But I thought you would know. I'm not going to ask my mother, are you?'

'No! Not considering the circumstances.'

'Can you see now how important it is that we get married straight away?'

'I don't agree with you, Jack. I haven't heard about all this before, but I'm sure you are wrong.'

'I don't think I am.'

'I want to wait and see,' Eunice spoke with stubbornness. 'I don't want to rush into this if there isn't any reason.'

'Any reason!' Jack exploded again. 'Don't you love me?'

'Not at the moment, I don't. Not with you shouting at me and pushing me about.'

Jack had nothing to say in his own defence. He had spoken harshly, and he had been physically rough. But he was also determined to do the decent thing. He was not willing to leave this young woman sullied without taking responsibility for what he had done.

What she had most feared was now upon her. Christine had walked into the library in search of a book, only to find the lord of the house seated by the window, almost as if he had been waiting for her to arrive.

'Ah! Miss Shore. What a pleasure to have you join me like this.' Charles' words were thick with an oily quality.

'I'm sorry to disturb you, sir,' Christine spoke quickly, beginning to back out of the room.

'Oh, please. Don't leave on my account. Come in. Take whatever it is you are looking for.'

Christine didn't want to stay. She wanted to flee the library. In fact, she wanted to flee the entire house.

This was one of those days that Colin and Emily had gone to an appointment, and for a change they had even taken the baby. Christine had hoped that the earl would also have gone out, but now, to her horror, she found that he was very much at home.

'I must apologise,' Charles began using a voice that might have charmed anyone else, but only served to repulse Christine. 'I have not had the opportunity to welcome you to my home. I have not seen my sister for a number of years, you understand, and there has been some misunderstanding between us.'

Christine wished she could accept his words as genuine, but her heart told her she could not.

'I know you must be very busy,' Christine's tone quavered as she began her excuse. 'I will just hurry along and find some quiet place to read in the garden.'

'Nonsense!' He contradicted her. 'I think it is high time that I showed you a little English hospitality. I would be most gratified to be able to show you about my home.'

No matter how much Christine wanted to decline the offer, she could not think of any sensible reason why she should not be obliging.

It was with a great deal of trepidation that she allowed the earl to take her arm and begin the tour. At first, he started to show her things on the lower floor; in the ballroom, the parlour; paintings and heirlooms of some value.

If someone had asked her, she would not have been able to repeat a single detail of the description because she was too involved with her own anxieties. Though he had not said anything wrong, nor had he done anything wrong, something warned the young woman that she was in grave danger.

And this intuition only increased when he insisted they look at the rooms on the upper floors.

'I've really taken up too much of your time already,' Christine tried one more desperate attempt at escape.

'On the contrary,' Charles gave what Christine thought was an evil-looking smile. 'I haven't even begun to show you the best part of the house yet.'

Many thoughts ran through Christine's mind. Would there be any point in pulling away and running to hide? Would there be any point in calling out for help? What would she say to the servants if they did respond to such a call? As she had already thought several times, the man had not actually said or done anything for her to be in such a panic, and yet she was.

As if Charles sensed her fear, he spoke on cue. 'You are far too tense, my dear. Relax! There shouldn't be this ridiculous distance between us. After all, we are practically related.'

Christine felt helpless, not wanting to offend the man for Emily's sake, and yet so afraid of some nameless evil that enveloped him. Still, she allowed herself to be guided along, and before she knew it, she found herself surveying the interior of the master bedroom.

'It is a most comfortable room,' she heard Charles' voice penetrating her mental turmoil. 'Perhaps you would like to sit on the bed?'

'No!' Christine burst out, forgetting any attempt at manners. 'This is not right!'

'What is not right?' Charles increased the strength of his grip on her arm.

'It is most improper for me to be here like this.' Christine had gained some confidence.

'Improper?' He seemed offended at the suggestion. 'I do believe that I am master of this house. It is I who determines what is proper and what is not.'

'I don't want to be here!' At last, Christine found enough courage to challenge him verbally.

'That is a shame, my dear,' his tone was now full of mockery, 'for I want you here, and I want to be able to show you some things I'm sure you haven't experienced before.'

At that, Christine did pull away, but she was too late to prevent him from closing the door, blocking her way of escape.

'You shouldn't be doing this,' she tried to bluff a confidence. 'Your sister would be most disappointed in you.'

'Shut up about my sister. I care nothing about her or her peasant husband. And I don't care about you either.'

It was at this point that Christine realised she was not the first young woman to have been put in this position by Charles Wallace.

She had never seen it before, but she recognised the burning evil in his eyes as lust, a look she would never forget for as long as she lived ...

CHAPTER 6

*T*here was nothing left to do now, Christine decided. She had already sought out a suitable travelling companion and had booked a passage for home. She knew that Emily and Colin would prevent her if they had known what she was doing, but she wasn't going to let them know. Not until it was too late to stop her.

As it was, Colin could very nearly have been hanged as a murderer. Emily had known this was a threat from the very moment she had discovered what her brother had done.

Perhaps, if Christine had been less strong and less determined, the evidence of her ordeal would not have been obvious, but her strong resistance to Charles Wallace's indecent assault had caused him to become incensed with a violent aggression that had left Christine beaten and bruised.

When Emily had returned from the day's outing, she had needed to go search for Christine, because she had not come down for the evening meal. When she finally found her, cowering and shivering behind her bed, Emily was shocked to the core.

She didn't need to ask to know what had happened, and she had instantly wanted to run away from the truth, but knew that if she didn't stand and take positive action, her husband would most assuredly try to kill her brother, and then the outcome would have been clear. Charles Wallace's influence was strong, and there would not have been a magistrate in the land who would not have at the very least jailed Colin Shore for the rest of his natural life.

Emily did all she could to conceal the crime against Christine. Without speaking to Colin, she arranged for all of them to be removed to a rented apartment. She kept Christine away from her brother, so that he would not know what had happened, and she kept this up until she had called her lawyer to be present.

Just as she had expected, when he did learn the truth, Colin was instantly prepared to go and kill his brother-in-law, and it was only the lawyer's sound common sense that was able to prevent him from doing something so totally foolhardy.

Christine had remained in a daze all that time, unable to think or do anything for herself, for over a week.

By the time her thoughts had begun to clear, she realised that nothing any of them could do would be able to bring Earl Wallace to justice. His power and influence as a member of the House of Lords was such that no one was prepared to take the word of a low-born foreigner against his.

Christine became aware that even though she had made plenty of noise, screaming for help against the attack, not one member of the household staff were willing to testify against their employer.

The conclusion she had finally drawn was that she had been cast a lot in life, and there was nothing that was going to change it.

She was lost and alone, and now she was going to go back to her own country to try and find some way to live out the rest of her God-forsaken days. She only hoped that they would not be many. The pain inside her was so great.

So now it was done. She had destroyed the ripped and blood-stained clothing, and she had determined in her mind that she would not think about the incident again.

To make certain of this, she avoided every opportunity of seeing her reflection in a looking-glass. She had accidentally seen her face just once, and the bruised and swollen eyes and lips were enough to set back her emotional recovery a good way. She didn't want anything to remind her of what had happened.

Once I have put thousands of miles of ocean between me and this cursed place, I will be able to feel normal again, she recited to herself. *I just want to forget that I ever set foot in London.*

It was so totally ironic. There would have been no possible way that Jack would have answered the letter from Christine if it had not been for the other letter he held in his hand. He read the second letter again, allowing the pain of what it meant to wash over his soul.

Dear Mr Browning,

I'm sorry if this letter causes you any inconvenience, but it is for the best.

As you well know, neither Mrs Booth nor myself ever approved of your attachment to our daughter, and so we were quite relieved when she asked us to allow her to travel to Melbourne.

Eunice has asked that we pass on her desire to let you know that she wishes to break off your engagement to her. We fully expect that she will be married to her cousin within the month.

This has been our dearest wish from the start, and we believe it is for the best. I hope you will understand that Eunice will be much happier married to someone of her own social standing.

Yours truly

Edward Booth

Just before the train pulled in at Flinders Street Station, Jack wondered if he would be able to find Eunice somewhere in this huge city, and he pondered on that thought for as long as it took to disembark.

But by the time he had carried his bag out into the open street, he let go all hope of such a venture. He had no idea where he could even start looking.

His thoughts turned to the other letter, and he opened it yet again to check the address he needed to find.

Dear Jack,

I was so wrong. You were right. The children need us. Will you meet me here and bring me back to Green Valley?

Christine

Yet again, Jack was puzzled. There was hardly anything to the letter. It was short and impersonal; totally lacking in warmth. He wondered just exactly why she had written to him and why she was not with her brother.

If his own heart had not been in so much turmoil, and he hadn't needed an excuse to get away from Green Valley, he would never have responded to such a letter. But as it was, he was now on his way to meet Christine Shore. What would result from that meeting was a total mystery to him.

After hailing a Hackney cab and giving the driver the address from Christine's letter, Jack settled back into the leather seat and, blocking out all thoughts of the houses that passed him, he turned his thoughts again to Eunice.

I don't understand what went wrong, he thought to himself. *She seemed so much in love with me. She wouldn't have let me touch her at all if she didn't love me, surely.* The thoughts seemed to tumble around in a fruitless search for answers.

But then he recalled just how much he had lost respect for her because of what she had allowed. *Perhaps she lost respect for me as well,* he pondered. *But I was willing to do the right thing. She shouldn't have just left me like that!*

But no matter how many times Jack went over the whole mixed-up affair in his mind, and no matter how many times he tried to think of a way of finding her, he always came to the same conclusion. By now, according to Eunice's father, she would be married. She would now be the wife of some important merchant, someone with lots of money and lots of social class.

I wonder if the new husband knows about us, Jack thought. *I wonder what he would say if he knew just how close we were.*

None of these thoughts gave him any satisfaction, but rather they caused a bitterness to grow in the young man's soul. By the time the driver had pulled the horse to a standstill outside the address given, Jack had allowed a good deal of anger and resentment to gain a place in his mind. Eunice Booth had betrayed him. She had seduced him, and then she had betrayed him.

Jack didn't know whether he would be able to trust a woman again.

***

Christine had been back in Melbourne for over a week now. On one hand she hoped that Jack would respond to her letter soon, and on the other she didn't care if he didn't.

During the many weeks aboard ship, Christine had carefully constructed a wall of hardness about her heart. No longer did she care if she appeared rude or indifferent to other passengers. She had no wish to allow anyone to be privy to her thoughts or her feelings. There was too much pain.

But as day followed day, Christine had learned how to block out the pain.

She went about all the necessary daily chores, ignoring most people, even the ones who had tried to offer her some form of friendship and encouragement. *What could they possibly know about how I feel?* she thought rebelliously on many occasions when she was justifying her cold manner to herself. *What do I care what they think of me? My life is over now, anyway. There is nothing left for me to live for.*

When the ship had docked at Port Melbourne, Christine had almost given way to tears. For a few short moments she felt an overwhelming relief to be back home, but just as quickly she hardened her thoughts and determined that she would not be found weak and vulnerable again.

She had decided that from now on no one was going to hurt her as Charles Wallace had done. No one was going to find her unable to defend herself.

When she had come ashore, she had thought about what she would do from there. The small amount of money she had taken from Emily was not going to support her in the city for very long, and yet she dreaded the thought of facing her mother again. Once again, she had fought to steel herself against tender thoughts of her family. *I cannot afford to go running back to them,* she recited to herself. *They will know what's happened the moment they see me. I won't give them the opportunity to cast me out. I will just shut them out of my heart, and then they won't be able to hurt me either.*

The decision to write to Jack was forced on her by necessity. If it had been at all possible, Christine would have hidden herself from everyone she knew for the rest of her life, but realistically this wasn't an option.

All those months back, before she'd left for England, Jack had made it quite clear that he didn't care about love. When

Christine recalled this fact, she decided that if he were still willing, she would do what she should have done from the start. She had no capacity to love any more; that had been forcefully stolen from her, along with her innocence.

But Christine felt that she could at least serve her niece and nephew. Jack would provide for them. He would see to it that they had food and shelter. *He didn't want my love*, Christine muttered to herself in justification again. *It won't matter to him if I have none to give.*

There were moments when panic threatened to set in. Christine was aware of just how little money she had left. She had not eaten for two days as it was; not that she had really wanted to eat. But the fact remained, that if Jack didn't respond within the next day or so, Christine would be forced to abandon her rented room, and she would have to find her own way back to Green Valley the best way she could.

She was tempted to pray, and ask that Jack would come, but she instantly cut off that thought. *If God were interested in me, he would have stopped Charles Wallace from having his way*, she thought angrily. *If God exists, he doesn't listen to my prayers.*

***

When Jack Browning finally came face to face with Christine Shore, he could not believe he was looking at the same girl whom he had known ten months before. He struggled to recall the youthful vibrancy that had always shone from her face, whether she was happy or even if she was in a temper. All that was left in its place was a dull look of resignation.

Jack knew that Christine was only a few months younger than himself, and yet he could have sworn that she had aged years instead of months. Her face was pale and sallow, and something more.

It only took a little while to put his finger on it. Her face was a mask of bitterness. He wanted to ask, but her look of hardness didn't seem to give him the opportunity.

'Is everything all right with your brother and his wife?' Jack felt it was a safe question to ask.

'They are well enough.' Christine shrugged her shoulders in a careless way, not wanting to divulge more information. She had to admit that she was relieved to see her former sparring partner, but she had no intention of letting him see that.

'I have to confess, I am a little surprised to hear from you. I sort of expected you to arrive back in Green Valley with Colin and his family, altogether.'

'They still had business that was dragging on. I was anxious to be home again, and so I made my own arrangements.'

'And Colin was happy with that?' Jack sounded sceptical.

'I need to come to the point, Jack,' Christine avoided the question. 'Before I left for England you made a proposal to me. I should have accepted you then.'

Jack stared, open-mouthed, amazed at what he was hearing. But he had no words to offer.

'Have you found someone to mother the children?' Christine asked, a small arrow of fear shooting through her mind. 'I would perfectly understand if ...'

'No!' Jack cut across her speech. 'No, there is no one else!' He dismissed Eunice from his thoughts with difficulty, knowing that even if she had married him, she would never have been a mother to the two children.

'You said it would be the happy solution for everyone, before.' Christine was fishing for a second chance. 'I can see now that you were right, if you are still open to the plan.'

'At the moment, the children are with my mother. Lord knows there isn't room for them, but things have been difficult for me the last couple of weeks.' Jack sighed wearily.

'Have you changed your mind about taking on Pete's responsibilities? It's a year since he passed away.'

'Let's just say I may have become confused recently,' Jack hedged. He was no more willing to be honest than she was. 'Are you saying that you will come back to Green Valley and take on the responsibility of the children with me?'

Christine nodded, fighting back the panic that was rising in the pit of her stomach.

'Are you saying that you want to marry me?'

This question was too much for Christine, and she turned and rushed from the room, into the dark hallway. She had no wish to marry anybody. She hated men. All men. Her father had deserted them when she was just a girl; Colin had failed to protect her when she most needed it, and then failed to seek the revenge she so craved, and then there was the earl.

All in all, if she had been able to find another way to survive, she would never have even spoken to Jack Browning. But here he was, as tall and as handsome as he had ever been, and yet she was repulsed by him.

'Why did you ask me to meet you here?' Jack's question broke into Christine's thoughts, and she realised that he had followed her into the hallway. 'If you just want a ride back to Green Valley, and your mother, then I will be happy to accompany you.'

'No!' Christine objected instantly. She would not go back to her mother's house. How could she now that she had fallen from grace?

'Well, what is it you want, Miss Christine Shore?' Jack had run out of patience. He was tired of being used, and yet he sensed that he was about to agree to the ultimate in being taken for granted.

'I'm just thinking of the children,' Christine lied. She had not thought of the twins for days.

'Then it's marriage you want – for the children's sake?'

'Yes!'

Jack looked at her long and hard. He knew that she was hiding something; but then he was hiding something too. Anyway, what difference would it make now? He was hurt and angry. He didn't love Christine Shore. He didn't think he would love any woman now. There was still the old vow he had made after the funeral. Christine was presenting an easy way to fulfil that duty. Despite the fact that there was no real happiness or joy attached to it, there was nothing to object to it either.

'All right,' he stated without feeling. 'We will marry. How long do you need to prepare?'

CHAPTER 7

Mr and Mrs Jack Browning sat silently and sullenly across from each other as the train clattered and rolled across the Victorian countryside, towards Green Valley. Neither of them were particularly inclined to speak, and both were reflecting on the events of the morning.

It had taken several days for Jack to make the arrangements, and it was a good thing as their combined funds could not have supported them in Melbourne for another day. So Jack and Christine had stood before a minister and had exchanged wedding vows, clearly lacking in emotion and depth. The minister, if he noticed, chose not to make a comment. Jack slipped a cheap wedding ring on his bride's finger, a symbol of convenience, nothing more. When they were invited to exchange the traditional kiss, Jack leaned over and brushed his lips across Christine's cheek. Even this flimsy gesture of affection brought waves of nausea to Christine's stomach, and she fought to keep a straight face. She had no wish to allow Jack to know just how much his touch revolted her.

By the time the train reached Brinsford, Jack realised that he was going to have to make other arrangements. He had ridden his horse the twenty miles from Green Valley, to meet the train. It was stabled at the livery in Brinsford, but now he realised that he would need another animal, or at least a vehicle of some sort, to transport his wife back to their home.

Neither Jack nor Christine had any more money, and without even discussing it, both knew what the other was thinking. There was no way that she would consider riding double. That arrangement brought too much physical closeness. She knew it would be hopeless them trying to walk the twenty miles in what was left of the day. They had no more money to rent a room for one of them to stay behind. All in all, they recognised the situation for what it was – awkward.

'We'll leave your luggage here,' Jack eventually announced. 'You can ride, and I'll walk.'

Christine was not about to argue. There was little alternative. And yet, after they had travelled for some way, she felt just a small measure of guilt.

'I'll walk for a while,' she offered. 'My legs could use the exercise.'

Jack accepted her offer without comment.

The moon was quite high in the sky by the time the pair began their descent into the valley. Both were hungry and tired, but neither of them complained to the other.

'We are so close now, it seems pointless us camping by the roadside,' Jack commented, as if Christine had asked a question. 'It would be quicker if we stopped by the Wallace estate. You will want to see your mother, I take it?'

Christine didn't want to see anyone, but she could see that it would take them an extra half an hour to make it out to Pete and Julianne's place. Stopping by at the great house would be the most sensible thing.

'I don't care what you do.' Her words sounded harsh, and Jack wondered at it. But he had already made up his mind. He was too tired and too hungry to pass up the opportunity of rest.

Christine was fighting a huge emotional battle by the time they walked up the gravel driveway in front of Wallace Hall. Part of her wanted to run to her mother's arms and have her rock and comfort her until the pain went away. But the other part screamed at her that she must not let down her guard. She must not allow anybody to see a weakness if she were to save herself from further hurt.

Automatically, Jack led his horse around the side of the house, to the massive stables. One of the young lads Colin had hired was asleep in the hay loft, and he climbed down to take the horse the moment Jack called out. Christine climbed down, her legs shaky and numb. It had been many months since she had sat on a horse, and to ride for four hours at a stretch would mean sore muscles come morning.

'Are you ready?' Jack allowed his tone to express a small degree of concern. He realised the importance of what they were about to do. Christine had not seen her mother in ten months, and she had not given her any warning that she was coming home, and to top it off, she had not given her any indication that she would bring a husband with her. 'Do you want to make the announcement, or shall I?'

As Christine heard Jack's kind offer, she felt an overwhelming urge to soften, tears stinging her eyes, but that insistent voice in the back of her mind demanded that she pull herself together and remain passive.

'Perhaps you will be able to say it better than I could,' Christine answered. 'Mother would take it better from you than me.'

'Christine,' Jack suddenly wanted to break through the wall between them. 'Is there something wrong? Something we should talk about?'

'There's nothing that anybody can do anything about,' Christine answered firmly and quickly. 'Let's just make this announcement, and then we can go home.'

The words, 'go home' might have sounded inviting if Christine had not had such a biting edge to her voice. Jack simply shrugged his shoulders and decided to return into his own shell of disillusionment.

⚜

Rose was stunned. At first she was overjoyed to see her second daughter home from her overseas journey. But that joy quickly melted away when she saw the physical symptoms of some traumatic ordeal.

'What has happened, Christine?' Rose allowed a depth of love and warmth to show in the way she spoke, and followed it up by taking Christine in her motherly embrace.

But Christine had ruthlessly schooled herself not to respond. She stood stiff and rigid, not yielding at all to her mother's welcome. Rose sensed this straight away, and pulled back to study her daughter's face. What she saw in Christine's eyes frightened her.

'Jack has an announcement to make,' Christine blurted out, to divert her mother's attention.

'Jack?' Rose turned her troubled gaze on the young man standing near the doorway.

'Christine and I were married this morning.' He spoke the words as someone who was delivering bad news.

'Married?' Rose was amazed still further, but she could not match her emotions with what such an announcement would usually warrant. Such occasions usually called for a celebration, but Rose could tell that something was not at all right about this wedding.

'Jack, I thought that you were engaged to …'

'Mr Booth has sent his daughter to Melbourne to be married to her cousin,' Jack gave the information quickly, not wanting dwell on it.

Christine heard this. It was the first she had been aware that there had been somebody else in his life, but she had been so tied up with her own emotional trauma that she had not noticed that Jack was different – that in fact he might have been hurting too. And she wasn't prepared to spend energy on that thought now. Nothing could be gained by her feeling sorry for someone else. She had to fight *her* own battles. Let him fight *his* own.

Rose, trying to take in all of the information, did the best she could in trying to appear pleased, not just that her daughter was home, but that they had finally decided to marry. She guessed that it was to become a family for the twins.

'And you have just come in from Brinsford?' Rose asked, putting aside all the other troubling thoughts.

'Yes! I only had my horse, so we've been taking it turns in walking and riding.' Jack took the responsibility for answering the questions. Christine didn't care. She had nothing left to say.

'It's very late! Have you eaten?'

'No,' Jack answered. 'We would be grateful if we could get a bite to eat before we go on home.'

'You can't go any further tonight,' Rose argued. 'You must stay here. Lady Vera is already in bed, but I know she would insist that you both stay.'

Neither of the newly-weds had the will to resist, so they allowed Rose to organise some food for them, and a room for them to share.

Just before Christine retired for the night, her mother tried once again to break the strange hardness that had enveloped her daughter. 'Colin shouldn't have let you travel home alone,' she commented as she tried to hug her. 'But I am glad to have you back, dear. I can see that you have had a hard trip. I do hope you will feel better in the morning.'

But no matter how optimistic Rose appeared to be, she could tell that it was going to take more than a good night's sleep to restore to her daughter what was lost.

This had been the hardest part. Christine wanted to shout and demand that her mother give her another room to sleep in. But to do this would be to admit that she didn't really want to be married to Jack, and from that admission Rose would conclude that Christine wanted to turn back time and be part of the family again.

It couldn't happen. Christine was not the happy-go-lucky innocent child she had been before she'd left. She was no longer a pure young woman, but she was an object of scorn and shame. She was dirty, and when her mother found out the truth, she would not want her any more. Christine refused to let herself be put in that place of rejection. She would reject them first.

Though Christine had forgotten how to be thankful, she at least noticed that Jack was prepared to give her all of the privacy and space she needed. Grudgingly, after he'd turned the lamp down, she crawled into the large double bed, and found herself a safe position lying as close to the edge as she could possibly go without falling off. She was absolutely determined not to get close enough to her husband to actually touch him. And subconsciously, she managed to hold this unyielding posture for the entire night.

She didn't wonder how Jack might interpret this obvious rejection. She didn't care about Jack. All she cared about was herself and her own pain.

As it was, Jack was too full of anger and pain of his own to really notice very much.

The second day of this uncomfortable marriage dawned with all the tension and hardness that had been a feature of the first. Jack spoke to his wife only those words that were necessary to making plans. Christine only answered direct questions. Already she resented Jack and for no more reason than that he was a man.

Rose did not fail to see that there was a lack of warmth and companionship that should have been at least the basic starting point of a marriage, even if it had been arranged for convenience sake. The concerned mother wanted desperately to say something, to force the younger people to take a long look at the way they were behaving towards one another, but every time she opened her mouth to speak, she lost courage.

They certainly did not present her with an invitation to give counsel, in fact, if their body language could have been put into speech, Rose should have assumed that they were telling her to mind her own business. There was nothing she could do for the moment, but she was determined to pray for them as a couple and as a family, considering that they would now be the parents of her two beloved grandchildren.

Leaving her mother and coming again to the home of her childhood were two more emotional hurdles that Christine was determined to overcome. As she climbed down from Jack's horse, she could see the graves of Julianne and Pete, and of her father in the distance, under the far-away tree. Still she resisted the urge to express any emotion. To be vulnerable was to be despised. It was going to take work, but she resolved that she would not feel anything, good or bad.

'Do you want to come with me over to my folks', to fetch the children?' Jack asked the question in passing, as if it didn't really matter to him.

'No!' Christine answered, and then as if it were a great concession, she added: 'I'll clean up the house and prepare some dinner for them when you get back.'

Jack nodded and turned towards the shed where he kept the wagon. He knew that he'd made a mistake in agreeing to Christine's plan to marry, but then it had been his own doing. He'd always declared self-righteously about how they should sacrifice their own desires out of respect for the memory of Pete and Julianne. A year ago, he had meant it. It had seemed like a noble act then.

But now he could tell that Christine had no noble intentions. He easily perceived her bitterness, but he could not understand why she had come back, nor why she had manipulated her way so determinedly into the present bizarre situation.

'I guess we will see if she does really care about the children,' he muttered to himself as he set off down the road. 'One thing is for certain, she doesn't seem to care about anything else.'

⚜

If there was only one thing in this world that Christine felt safe about, it was the two young children. As time passed, she allowed herself to be taken in by their baby charm. For them she didn't mind working hard, and when Julianne, the more boisterous of the two, was particularly hard to get on with, Christine seemed to relish the challenge. In the one-year-old girl, Christine found a mirror of what she had been like before disaster had overcome her.

Because Jack found it easier to stay outside working for every daylight hour, Christine found she could behave quite naturally with the children. Though she never laughed outwardly any more, she frequently found herself tempted to smile at the two youngsters.

Neither of them were as yet able to speak, but Christine could see that they communicated between themselves, as she watched them plan and carry out some piece of mischief together. Pete would always allow his sister to take the lead, and therefore it was always Julianne who found herself in confrontation with her foster mother.

These times were the only bit of real life Christine permitted for herself. By the time Jack came inside to eat, he would find the children ready to be tucked up in their beds, and he would find his dinner set out for him in solitary state on the kitchen table.

Christine made no attempt at conversation, and she made it clear that she was unwilling even to sit with him. She would leave him to eat while she finished putting the children to bed and then she would silently wash up his dishes. Then, without a word, she would go off to the bedroom by herself.

She didn't want him to follow her, and he didn't. She wanted to be in bed and fast asleep by the time he'd unwound for the evening, and was ready to go to bed.

To Christine, this seemed to be the happiest she had felt since that dreadful incident in England. She gave no thought to her husband, justifying to herself that his meals were cooked, his clothes were clean and mended, and the children were well and truly looked after. What more could he ask?

But to Jack, there was more. He had visited his family on several occasions, just so that he could have some conversation. He was too proud to try and force from his wife this simple act of friendship. She had made it quite plain that she wanted nothing to do with him, and so he made all kinds of excuses to his mother when he appeared for no particular reason.

'How are you and Christine settling in with the children?' Elizabeth asked kindly, not really aware of the strained relationship that existed.

'The children are doing really well,' Jack answered truthfully. Though Christine had been ignorant of his watching from outside, Jack had seen the way she was open and caring with the two little ones. It was a fact he was thankful for on the one hand, and jealous of, on the other.

'You must both come over for dinner sometime,' his mother went on, unconscious of his straying thoughts. 'Perhaps you could bring the family to worship with us on Sunday, and stay after.'

'I will have to ask Christine.' Jack was evasive. He doubted that his wife would want to fellowship with anyone at all. They had not been to service at the church since they had been back, and the only time they had seen Christine's family was when Rose had made the effort to come out to visit her daughter. Christine had become a hermit in her own home, and appeared to like it that way.

As Jack rode back across the miles to Pete's farm, which had now become his own, he began to think about Christine – his wife. In the weeks that she had been living with him, he had seen some health return to her face. She was less pale, and her eyes showed just a little more spark than they had when he'd met her in Melbourne.

Jack had become used to the silent resentment that was always there, and so he began to disregard it. Christine Shore had always been an attractive girl. She'd always had a fiery temper, not unlike the one his young niece was now displaying, and yet this had only enhanced her personality, Jack decided.

The bitterness she now wore did not become her, and Jack felt he was tired of bowing to its demands. There had been times in the past when he and Christine had shared moments of close friendship. A year or so ago, when he'd first proposed this particular scheme, Jack had felt that he was prepared to love this girl. He was certain that he would have succeeded then, but now his confidence was seriously shaken.

And moreover, he didn't like the way that they were strangers sleeping in the same bed. As he stabled his horse, and brushed it down, he determined that he was going to make an attempt to break the barrier that existed between himself and his wife.

Just as he'd anticipated, Christine had laid out his evening meal, and she was standing ready to let him greet the children. For once, Jack did not avoid her gaze, but deliberately caught it, wondering what he would see. Christine was surprised by the direct look, and quickly averted her eyes, fussing over the toddlers to cover any wayward emotion.

'Your father's home,' she muttered needlessly, picking up Julianne ready to hand to Jack for his ritual kiss goodnight. The little girl was eager to go to her uncle, who was more like a daddy to her. She loved the attention she always got from him. Christine was thankful when Pete started up a jealous whimper. He wanted to be picked up by Jack as well, and so Christine was able to withdraw from the trio and escape the unwelcome attention Jack had given her.

She was tempted to go straight to bed herself. She didn't want any openness with her husband. But she knew it was her job to tuck the children up, and see that they were properly settled. So she waited quietly, watching Jack bounce the children about on his knee for ten minutes or so, before moving in to end their fun.

'It's time for bed.' She spoke sternly, as she always did when Jack was around. She didn't want him to think that she had ever enjoyed her time with the twins. 'Come along.' Pete and Julianne were used to their foster mother's strict bed-time routine now, and the fight to stay was never convincing.

Jack sighed as he relinquished the pair. His longing for real family relationship seemed to rise up like a wave. As he moved across to the table to eat his tea, he found himself planning what he would say to his wife when she emerged from the children's room. But when she did come back, closing the wooden door behind her, there was that cold, impenetrable wall surrounding her whole being, so he didn't say a single thing of what he'd decided, although he wasn't entirely ready to be defeated yet, either.

He let her pick up his dishes, as she usually did, but instead of retreating to the rocker in the corner, Jack followed her to the sideboard and picked up the tea-towel, ready to help.

'What are you doing?' Christine snapped, annoyed.

'I'm going to wipe the dishes after you've washed them,' Jack answered innocently.

'I don't need your help! I can do it on my own!'

'I know that,' Jack attempted a smile he hoped was helpful to his cause. 'I just thought you might like some company.'

'I don't need any company,' Christine barked, turning her back on him, and thrusting her hands into the soapy dishwater.

'Maybe not,' Jack shrugged, 'but I do.'

Christine didn't have anything to say to this revelation. *Why does he have to mess up my carefully arranged routine?* she fumed to herself. *We were getting on perfectly well before.*

Jack watched her as she put unnecessary force into the scrubbing of the dishes. He could tell she was angry with him for breaking their routine code of behaviour. Still, he was determined to try one more time.

Laying the tea towel aside, he placed his hands on her shoulders, hoping to turn her to face him. He felt her body tense, yet he was firm in his pre-formed decision. Suddenly he was overtaken by an urge to kiss her, and he leaned forward, brushing her hair lightly with his lips. But if he thought this would bring a tender response he was wrong.

Christine wrenched herself free of his hold, and turned a fierce eye on him. 'Don't you ever touch me again,' she hissed.

'I'm sorry.' Jack was truly surprised at the violence of her reaction. 'I didn't mean to alarm you. I don't want to hurt you, you know.'

'I don't know!' Christine's stance was defensive, and she threatened him with her eyes.

Jack was confused and suddenly doubtful, and so he withdrew from the situation. Christine waited for him to back away before she went straight to the bedroom, the tea dishes forgotten. She didn't expect Jack to follow, but he did for a change. 'I'm sorry to have frightened you like that,' he spoke again, hoping that she had calmed down.

'Don't come near me, Jack,' Christine cautioned. 'Just leave things as they were, and we will get on just fine.'

'I can't do that any more,' he spoke resolutely, but when he did, he thought he saw a flash of abject fear cross her face. 'Look, Christine,' he began to promote his cause, 'we have been married for nearly two months now, and I haven't touched you once, but ...' He paused, wondering what it was that caused such panic to appear on her whole countenance. 'I think perhaps you should talk to your mother, you know, about us.'

'I don't need to talk to my mother,' Christine contradicted. 'I'm doing just fine as I am.'

'You are!' Jack agreed. 'I have seen you with the twins, and you are doing a fine job, but ... it's just that, there is more to a marriage than what we currently share. A relationship between a man and a woman. Your mother could explain that to you.'

'I don't need my mother to explain that to me. I know all about it!' Christine released more than she had intended, but it was too late.

'What do you mean?' Suddenly Jack was defensive.

'What do you think I mean?' Christine was on the attack now, as her only means of defence.

'Has your mother told you about ...'

'No! She hasn't.'

'Then how could you know what I'm talking about?'

'I've learned from cold, hard experience, Jack. How do you like that?'

Jack felt as if he'd been punched in the stomach, and a chill went down his spine. 'Are you telling me that you've been with a man before?' He asked the question tentatively, hoping that he was wrong, but to his dismay, she only offered a sneering, sickly smile, and turned from him.

'Have you?' He raised his voice and moved closer to her, forcing her to face him. 'I want to know the truth, Christine Shore.'

'Do you?' She challenged him. 'Do you really want to know? What difference will it make when you do?'

'You have, haven't you?' Quite suddenly, all Jack could see was Eunice's teasing, sensuous smile, and with this vision came the pain and the anger. He turned from his wife and fled the room, fury burning in his belly.

Once he broke into the cool, dark night, he let a yell of emotional tension break from his lungs, and then he found himself kicking the side of the house.

Perhaps he had been aware of the anger that had been building in him since the time of Pete's death, but now, with Christine's careless announcement, it had all been released. He was engulfed with rage, and he knew that it was not safe to stay in the house. He wanted to take all his anger out on somebody, and if he stayed here, he knew that Christine would be the most likely target.

To his credit, he elected to mount his horse, bareback, and ride out into the night.

Christine had not seen Jack for two days. She didn't know nor did she care where he was or what he was eating. In actual fact, Jack had been sleeping in the hay shed, the way he used to do when Ivy and Christine had been staying temporarily. He had not eaten much, only a meal that his mother had offered him when he'd gone to visit during the afternoon of the first day's absence.

When Jack walked back into the house, Christine looked up, determined not to show any fear or vulnerability.

'Who was it?' Jack spoke fiercely, ignoring the passage of two whole days and continuing the troubled conversation of two nights before. 'Or has there been more than one?'

'I don't have to answer that question,' Christine tried to avoid the subject.

'You do have to. I'm your husband. I have a right to know.'

'I don't want to talk about it.' Christine cast a worried glance over her shoulder towards the children's bedroom.

'Tell me, Christine, did you seduce him? Did you flirt with him, and entice him with your body?' Jack had been replaying the relationship between him and Eunice over and over in his mind, ever since he'd found out that Christine was no longer pure.

'What difference does it make to you, Jack?' Christine flared. 'I didn't promise you anything. I never told you that

I was clean. All you wanted was a mother for the children. I'm doing the job. Let's just leave it at that.'

'I won't leave it at that!' Jack was shouting now. 'You're no better than one of those prostitutes from one of those whore-houses in Melbourne.'

'Have you visited one of those whore-houses?' Christine became malicious, forgetting about the children in the other room. 'Has some prostitute seduced you, Jack Browning?'

'You disgust me!' Jack delivered his final judgement and was about to walk out of the house again when he was arrested by the sight of his mother-in-law coming into the kitchen from the children's room.

Rose's face was red with anger, her lips pinched tight with forced self-control. She had a child under each arm, and without looking at either Jack or Christine, she took both of them out of the front door.

Christine watched with horror knowing exactly what her mother was doing, and why. She wanted desperately to call out to her, to stop her. But she could not find her voice any more.

Jack watched Christine with contempt. Every part of him wanted to hate her for what she had done to him. It was no longer a case of what Eunice had done. Christine was now the target of all his blame. He wanted to make her feel every ounce of the anger and resentment he felt, whether she was actually the cause of it or not.

Rose had been gone from the room for a few minutes before she returned, a look of stubborn anger still fixed firmly in place.

'Mum,' Christine made a half-attempt to explain.

'I don't want to hear it, Christine. I have heard enough.' She pushed past her daughter and son-in-law to the small side room, and began to snatch up some clothes and toys that belonged to the twins. 'I will not leave my grandchildren here to be subjected to this kind of immorality!' She spoke firmly, and then she walked smartly, arms loaded, out to her waiting horse-drawn trap. Nothing more was said as she snapped the reins and urged the horse into a brisk trot.

Jack strode angrily from the house, slamming the door after him. Here was one more thing he could blame Christine for. It didn't occur to him that he had seen Rose's vehicle waiting in the front of the house, or he might have controlled the way he had spoken. But as it was, Christine was the cause of all his troubles, and now the object of his total scorn.

Left alone in the middle of the small kitchen, Christine wanted very much to cry. But she had spent so long walling up her emotions that she didn't know how any more.

All she could think about was the children. *Don't take them from me*, she agonised over and over in her mind. *They are all I have left. They are the only ones who understand me.*

CHAPTER 8

*T*here was nothing left for Christine to care about any more. She was alienated from her family, she was despised by her husband, and she no longer had any purpose to live.

She didn't bother with looking after Jack any more. Anything she did try to do for him he mocked and refused it as if she were the devil himself. She drifted through the painful days and nights like a lost child. She hardly ever ate, thinking that maybe she would die, sooner or later.

Jack decided that he was not going to be cast out of his bed because of what she'd done, so he told her to get out. Christine, with nowhere else to go, made up a bed for herself on the floor of the children's room, not bothering to rise from it until Jack was well and truly out of the house. Even then, she had no energy to do anything. She didn't bother to wash her hair, or her clothes.

By the time the reverend and his wife, Kate Laslett, came to see her, she was as near death as any starving beggar on the streets of London.

'You take her in the house and clean her up,' John ordered his wife. 'I want to have a few words with the husband.'

Kate's heart was twisted in grief at the sight of the girl who had been so beautiful and full of life not so long ago. They had found Christine fallen down by the creek, too weak to get up, and with no will to do so.

'What have they done to you?' Kate asked, tears spilling down her cheeks. She didn't expect Christine to answer, instantly recognising that she was not in her right mind. 'You poor girl. You poor, poor girl.' Kate was overcome with the emotion of it all. She had heard that the young couple were having problems, and she'd heard Rose's account of why the children were staying with her at the great house. But Kate had no idea that Christine had slumped so far into degradation and despair.

With a heavy heart, Kate set about putting her charge to bed. The temptation was to wash her first, so sadly had fallen Christine's state of hygiene, and even Kate had to admit that she smelt pretty bad. But in the end, the minister's wife elected to try to feed her some broth, a task which proved to be quite difficult with the patient weak and wishing to die. Finally, she had managed to spoon some nourishing stock down Christine's throat, and then she had followed her initial instincts to help the girl wash and change into something clean.

The whole process was a tax on Kate's spirits and when she had finished, she was tempted to just sit down and cry. But looking about the small dwelling, she saw that its state reflected the troubled state of the two young people who lived there. Without thinking about it, Kate proceeded to put the sad little house back into some semblance of order.

During the hours that it took his wife to accomplish this, John set about his own task. He walked furiously out to the paddock where he found Jack cutting some wood.

'I want you to come with me,' John spoke more harshly than he'd ever had cause to before.

'What for?' The rebellion was quite evident in Jack's response.

'Colin Shore is back from England, and you need to talk to him.'

'I don't want to have anything to do with her family,' Jack blurted out. 'She is a slut, and I'm finished with her.'

John didn't wait to think if hitting a parishioner was acceptable practice for a clergyman, but managed to send Jack Browning reeling backwards from the blow.

'You are a fool, young man,' John shouted angrily, 'and when you've heard what Colin has to say, you will need to make up a lot of ground. Now get on your horse, and hurry up.'

To be truthful, Jack had never in his life seen another man so certain of himself, and for a moment, he began to be afraid of what he had done. But his self-assurance soon returned once he was on horseback, following the minister along the road. He didn't say anything out loud, but his thoughts were murderous with regard to his wife, and her family.

It took a good half hour to reach the great house, and when they did, John ordered Jack to stay on his horse, while he went inside to find Colin. When the pair emerged on the front steps, Jack seriously began to doubt himself. Colin's eyes were ablaze with anger, and he could see that it was only the minister's restraining hand that was forcing Colin to control his urge to physically attack.

'I want the both of you to come to the manse, now! A horrible tragedy has occurred, and neither one of you is helping it by irresponsible temper,' John decreed, ignoring the irony of his statement.

The next two hours passed with the three men involved in a highly strained exchange of words. There was shouting, and tears, and angry physical displays as first Colin, and then Jack punched at inanimate objects. Through it all, John enlightened Jack as to what had happened to Christine Shore.

'She was your responsibility,' Jack said with angry energy. 'Why didn't you protect her?'

'Why didn't you?' Colin retorted instantly. 'What have you been doing to her in the last few months?'

'Yes, but I didn't know about this,' Jack defended. 'She was acting like a ...'

'Like a what?' Colin had risen from his seat, tense as a coiled spring.

'We are not getting anywhere like this,' John had interrupted. 'It's long past the time for casting blame. Now is the time to act positively.'

'What's to be done now?' Colin spoke with an air of hopelessness. 'No one wants a soiled wife.'

'I already have her,' Jack responded in a flash. 'And there doesn't seem to be any choice about it now, does there!'

'You are both going to have to calm down,' John insisted again. 'Christine is the victim of a violent crime. She is not a piece of baggage to be thrown aside now that she has been tattered. She needs healing.'

'Can such a thing ever be healed?' Colin asked doubtfully.

'I serve the God and Creator of the whole universe,' John spoke with conviction. 'If he can do all that, I'm sure he must be able to restore what has been stolen from your sister.'

'Perhaps,' Colin sounded doubtful.

'This is not something that will ever be talked about,' John went on to explain, once the two younger men had settled back. 'It's not something that polite society wants to know about, but the fact remains that your sister, Colin, is in a very unstable condition. Jack has made some serious mistakes, and he and I are going to talk about that in a while.

'As for you, I believe you will need to tell your mother. She will not want to know about it, of course, and she will probably want to sweep the information under the carpet. If that's what she wants to do, then let her, but at least she might understand Christine's behaviour just a bit more.'

'But I feel so responsible for what happened,' Colin sounded truly grieved, now turning the focus on to his own failures. 'It was my fault that she was left alone. I didn't think that Emily's brother would do such a thing.'

'Why didn't you do something?' Jack accused again, still upset. 'You should have tried to punish him in some way.'

'You are not in a position to be making accusations, Jack,' John spoke sternly to him.

'Emily hid the crime from me,' Colin went on to explain anyway. 'When I found out, I swore I'd kill the man. They had to physically restrain me, or I would've.'

'You should've,' Jack avowed. 'I would have!'

'And you would've been hanged, just like they would've hanged me. The man's an earl. He has more influence in that accursed city than any of us put together.'

Jack retreated, sullenly. He had heard what Colin had said, and he had understood. But now came the awful realisation of what he had done. To cover up his own dreadful wrongdoing, he wanted to blame Colin, but John would not hear of it.

'I don't think there is anything else you can do now, Col,' John offered as a way of dismissal. 'Jack and I need to talk some more about some other matters. Will you be all right?'

'I don't think I'll ever be all right,' Colin answered pessimistically. 'It might be easy for others to pretend this hasn't happened, but for me it's real, constantly hounding me day and night.'

Colin wasn't the only one who felt this awful guilt. Now Jack began to see the same dark cloud descending upon himself, and this only worsened when the minister returned from seeing Colin to the door.

'Now, sir,' John began, unyielding in his tone. 'What have you to say for yourself?'

Jack instinctively knew that making excuses was not going to be accepted by the minister, and so he remained silent, a pout on his face.

'There is more to this saga than we've just heard, isn't there?' John hoped to get to the bottom of the matter. 'This goes back a lot further than when you married Christine, doesn't it?'

Jack nodded, his defences weakening.

'How far back?' John pushed. 'What sort of blame have you been laying at your wife's door?'

'If God hadn't taken Pete, none of this would've happened,' Jack suddenly burst out. 'He should've left us alone, and then I wouldn't have done what I did.'

'So, now you want to shift the blame from your wife to God, is that it?'

'I couldn't save Pete. I prayed ... I prayed hard that God would save him, but he didn't! Why didn't he? Why did he have to take him like that?'

'And what else is there, Jack?' John was beginning to see the depth of the young man's anger and guilt, but he knew there was more. 'What happened between you and the Booth girl?'

'I couldn't help it,' Jack excused, his eyes wild with panic at having to confess. 'She was like Delilah, always at me, touching me, begging me to touch her in return. What's a man supposed to do?'

'So you had relations with her?' John asked, pained to realise just how far Jack had gone.

'It was her fault. She seduced me!'

'All right, Jack!' John changed his approach to one of calm acceptance. 'I think I begin to see your pain. Let's have a cup of tea, and then we can talk about what we can do to set things right.'

'It can't ever be set right,' Jack argued, not so willing to be pacified. 'I can never get Pete back, and I can never be clear in my conscience again. What I've done is so awful that I don't think even God himself could forgive me.'

'Well, there you have a starting point, Jack,' John gave a tentative smile, which confused his companion. 'The fact that you've admitted that you've done wrong is half our battle. Now that we've come to that point, the rest will follow along nicely!'

***

Jack felt a severe attack of guilt when he rode up to his house, accompanied by the minister. They had talked for the better part of two hours before John suggested they make their way back to the farm. The drama was far from over, but it seemed that there was no more that could be gained by prolonging this particular interview.

Now here they were, ready to walk into the house as bold as you please, hoping that no one would notice that anything was amiss. But plenty was amiss in Jack's mind. It was true that he had made a start towards restoration. John had encouraged him to pray and ask God to forgive him. This had been a big step considering the many blasphemous things Jack had thought and said. He had wondered if God could really overlook such huge offences.

'I just don't understand why God had to take my brother!' Jack had stated, before relinquishing the anger he'd held towards his Maker.

'There are some things in this life that not one of us could possibly find the answer for,' John had spoken gently, but with conviction. 'This is one of those things,' he said. 'But I want to share something with you, Jack,' John had continued. 'Though I have asked God the same question myself on a number of occasions, I know that cutting off my line of communication with him by bitterness and resentment will never make this life better. Those attitudes never really bring us any satisfaction. We don't really pay God back for what we perceive is wrong. All we ever end up doing is destroying our own lives.'

'If only I could just understand a little bit,' Jack sounded wistful now.

'It's a little bit like standing on that great lookout rock, high above the valley,' John began to explain. 'From there, a person can see the whole valley; all the roads, and all the farms. But from down here, we can only see one piece of scenery at a time, and only as we travel through the countryside can we begin to know the whole region.

'God knows our whole life. He sees the beginning and the end all at once. He knows how the whole life experience works out. We can only see one day at a time as we pass through life.'

'That's easy for you to say,' Jack sounded as if he wanted to be convinced. 'You're a minister. It's easy for you to understand these things. It's different for me.'

'We are not so different, Jack, you and I.' John didn't bother to complicate the explanation any more. He felt he'd said enough for one day. Besides, they were now at the house and ready to go in.

'You will stay for a while?' Jack asked, anxiety evident in his face.

'For a while, perhaps. It depends on how your wife is faring.'

Jack was not comforted particularly. He didn't want this confrontation. He would just as soon have run away and left all he owned to rot rather than face Christine with all of her hurt; that which she'd brought with her, as well as that which he'd caused. But John obviously had no doubt that it was time to open up the situation. He walked inside the small dwelling with confidence, leading his young friend towards an appointment with destiny.

Christine became aware that she was no longer alone. She had drifted in and out of an uneasy sleep for some time. Somewhere in the back of her clouded mind she realised that her wish to die had not been fulfilled, but that someone had rescued her.

She knew that someone was definitely not Jack. She had been too tired to think the situation through, but now, her natural curiosity got the better of her, and she opened her eyes to see who it was standing over the bed.

'I don't know what to say.' Jack's voice cracked with emotion when he saw her staring at him.

'It doesn't matter, Jack,' Christine answered weakly. 'I'm not worth the energy spent worrying.'

Jack wanted to talk, but he knew that he was pitifully inadequate. He had been an absolute monster; had treated her badly instead of being a comfort in her time of distress. He could not look at her wasted appearance and not feel all the guilt that had been plaguing him ever since he'd decided to 'confess'.

'I can't do this, John.' He cast a desperate plea across the room.

Christine became aware that the reverend and his wife were also crowded into the small room, watching the interaction. *So it was Mrs Laslett who stole my chance to die*, she thought miserably.

'Christine,' Kate broke the tense atmosphere by calling her attention. 'Do you feel strong enough to talk with us for a while?'

'It's too late for talk,' Christine brushed the idea aside. 'You should have let me die. It would have been best for all of us.'

'Can't you talk some sense into her?' Jack pleaded, his eyes intense with a mixture of frustration and fear.

'It will take a little time, Jack,' John counselled. 'You might make a start by telling her what we talked about earlier, don't you think?'

'I don't know how,' Jack complained. 'What should I say?'

'We will leave you alone for a little while,' Kate took John's arm to urge him out of the room. 'Just speak what's on your mind, Jack. That will do for now.'

The minister and his wife retreated graciously, leaving Jack full of apprehension. He looked at Christine, who had closed her eyes again. He could not tell whether she had fallen back asleep or if she was deliberately trying to shut him out. Either way, it presented him with time to muster courage, which was not an easy task when he studied her appearance.

What have I done to her? he asked himself silently. *What have I done?*

***

Once away from the tormented young couple, Kate could not contain her emotion any longer, and she sought her husband's tender embrace.

'I haven't seen anyone so close to hopelessness before,' she said, over the top of her tears. 'What happened to her, John? What dreadful thing has caused her to want death so badly she would try to take her own life?'

'Things happened in England,' John spoke quietly. 'Colin told me all about it.'

'What things?' Kate persisted, not satisfied that anything could be bad enough to reduce someone to such depths.

'It's not the kind of thing I want you to hear about,' John was sensitive in his refusal. 'It's bad enough that anybody should know at all.'

'But this is Christine, John! What has happened to her? Please, I need to understand.'

'You'll not think any less of her for knowing?' John asked, pulling back from his wife, and searching her face for assurance.

'Of course not! How could I? Has she done something wrong?' A small fear began to stir in Kate's heart as she began to imagine possibilities.

'No! Not at all!' John contradicted. 'Oh, Kate, my love. I don't want to repeat this horrible news again. It will break your heart, and it's already done enough damage to Christine and Jack. Not to mention Colin and Emily.'

'You're not reassuring me at all,' Kate began to look afraid.

Even as John struggled to find the right words to use, tears began to gather in his eyes. When he had been determined to make Jack understand, he had been fuelled by anger, but now he was beginning to feel his parishioners' pain and torment. Now he was starting to appreciate just how much of a tragedy this crime was, and the last thing he wanted to do was go over the sordid details again. But Kate was watching him, anxious for an explanation, and though he knew that it would pain her, he was compelled to help her understand what depth of trauma they would be dealing with when trying to help this young couple.

The telling was not easy. To utter the unspeakable took a lot of willpower. Several times John pleaded to cease the narrative, but his wife insisted she had to understand. When he had finished, he saw shock and revulsion in Kate's expression.

'I knew I shouldn't have told you,' he muttered quietly. 'You shouldn't have to ever hear of such depravity.'

'But it happened to our Christine,' Kate argued, emotion choking her voice. 'Why should I live in blissful ignorance while she suffers the consequences firsthand?'

'Would that such a crime never happened in the first place,' John spoke angrily.

'But it did happen,' Kate mourned openly now. 'No wonder she wanted to die. Even with Jack to support her.'

'Jack?' John's head came up as that subject caught his attention. 'No! Jack has not supported her, Kate. In fact the opposite. He believed her to be ... well, how can I say it?'

'What? Oh, John don't tell me he thought she was being unfaithful to him.'

'Perhaps. Probably worse. Anyway, it doesn't matter now. I have corrected his misconceptions.' A smile played about the corners of John's mouth as he spoke.

'I can't find anything at all that we should smile about.' Kate seemed annoyed at her husband's apparent insensitivity.

'Oh! I'm sorry.' John sought to retrieve the situation. 'If you knew what I was thinking, you would perhaps understand the smile.'

'What could you possibly be thinking that would excuse such an inappropriate response?' Kate wanted to know.

'Speaking of inappropriate. You should have seen just how it was that I managed to get Jack's attention. You see he wasn't really ready to have any misconceptions corrected.'

'John! What did you do?'

'It was not very Christian of me. In fact, I really must beg his forgiveness.'

'What have you done?' Kate was feeling most unsettled.

'I punched my young parishioner in the mouth. It was rather a good blow, actually. It sent him flying.'

Kate's hand flew to her mouth and the horror registered clearly on her face as she looked at her husband with tear-filled eyes.

'It's all right, my love,' John reassured his wife. 'I will apologise to Jack. I have no wish to take up boxing.'

Because Jack had not spoken for some ten minutes, Christine wondered if perhaps everyone had left the room, and she eventually opened her eyes to see. When she saw her husband still standing by the side of the bed, his troubled eyes fixed firmly on her face, she was somewhat shaken.

'If you want your bed back, I can go. I meant to die this time and be out of your way forever.' Her words were tinged with sarcasm, and she had meant them to hurt.

But Jack saw her in a whole different light now. It was not the goodness in his own heart, for heaven knew that he was as weak as the next man; it was more a gift of compassion that seemed to have come to him when he'd cried out to God for help. And because of this grace, Jack didn't register the pain intended by the remark.

'Colin and I spoke today.' He eventually made a start, speaking as purposefully as he could. 'I know what happened in England.'

'I don't want to hear about England,' Christine's voice rose in a high-pitched objection. 'I don't want to hear about Colin.'

'Maybe not, but I have to speak about it anyway.'

'No!' Christine covered her ears. 'No, Jack! Please don't. I can't bear to hear of it.'

'We have to talk about it, Christine,' Jack knelt down to her level and pulled her rigid hands away from her head. 'You have to listen to me. Do you hear me?'

Christine struggled against him for a few seconds, and he released her, surprised by her strength. She turned her back and put her hands over her head as if she were trying to protect herself from a falling object.

'It's my fault, Christine,' Jack sounded desperate now. 'I didn't know what had happened, and I assumed ... No! That's not it either. I was trying to blame you for something that I had done. You aren't the only one who's had experience, Christine. I thought I was going to marry the girl, but that was no excuse. I let her entice me into physical relations which I should have reserved for you.'

Christine shivered at the very thought. She had no wish for physical contact of any kind with Jack or any other man.

'I don't know what else to say.' Jack was feeling helpless. There had been no sign of acknowledgement or response. 'I'll try to make it up to you somehow, Christine,' he made a final attempt. 'I'm so sorry I didn't understand. I should have understood.'

With that last feeble attempt, Jack got up from his knees and left the room, feeling utterly defeated.

CHAPTER 9

❦

Christine had regained some physical strength. But no matter how hard any of her family had tried, she had refused to allow anyone admittance beyond the barrier she had erected to protect herself.

Only the reverend and his wife, and Colin and Emily knew about Christine's ordeal. Colin had tried to tell his mother, but she had not wanted to hear. These sort of things were not the subject of polite conversation, and so Colin had to be content with enduring a lecture about how he should have seen to it that his sister was properly looked after. Rose concluded on her own that Christine's change of attitude was due to the trauma of travelling.

'God never meant us to be traipsing all over the earth. It must take its toll on all of us,' and she dismissed the topic easily.

Jack was a different man. He had not made any more effort to force unwanted conversation upon his wife, but he was thoughtful and caring to a fault. It was as if he felt that penance could be paid by extra attention given to the small details.

But Christine gave his efforts no recognition. She refused to admit to herself that he was worth any acknowledgement. She had returned to the routine of cooking and cleaning, but talking and responding was way outside of the realms of where she felt in control.

In her heart, she grieved for the loss of the two children. They had been the only aspect of her tattered life where she had allowed any emotion to flow at all, and now her mother had taken them away from her. She did not expect that Rose would let them come back, even if she had asked for them; not now that she knew how low her daughter had descended.

And so Christine accepted the fact that she was allotted the lonely role of servitude. Jack meant nothing to her, and she was angry with Colin and Emily, so she had cut off any relationship with them.

To her, it was Emily's brother who had committed the unthinkable, and to some extent, Christine held that against Emily as well. As for Colin, Christine felt just a small measure of spiteful satisfaction in trying to make him pay for his negligence.

'But Colin didn't do anything to hurt you,' Jack had argued with her in one of their rare interactions. 'Why should you turn them away from visiting you? Your own brother and sister-in-law?'

'He's no brother to me,' Christine exclaimed bitterly. 'If he'd really cared, he would've done something to protect me from that monster. And then, when he did find out, he did nothing to make him pay for what he'd done. Nothing!'

'He couldn't, Christine,' Jack was frustrated, trying to defend Colin's position. 'If he'd tried ...'

'I don't want to hear about it!' Christine had flung this now familiar sentence at her frustrated husband, and marched out of the house, putting sufficient space between them to prevent him from pressing the issue.

Jack had tried to control his temper with her, but there were times when he felt that the situation was next to impossible. Christine had become absolutely closed to input from either him, or any of her family. Even the reverend and his wife had difficulty in carrying on a normal conversation without her getting up and walking out.

Jack felt that at least he was making some headway in his own relationship with God – he was praying more, and finding more peace in areas of earlier turmoil. But with Christine, he almost felt as if his prayers were falling on deaf ears.

Sometimes he wondered if it would be acceptable for him to run away from his responsibility as a husband and provider. But when he considered the example of his own father, husband and provider for twelve children, through good times and bad, he simply could not just disappear. At least John Laslett provided much needed encouragement for him during the really low times.

'We need to keep believing, Jack,' John had said over and over. 'Christine was always a good girl before. There's this wall now, but there must be a way to break through. God will show us a way.'

But just when Jack thought that nothing else could possibly go wrong for him, it happened.

He had been out in the scrub cutting timber, and stripping it, making it into useable poles for a new cattle yard. One of his brothers had been helping him load the wooden poles on the back of the wagon, and when the load was full, they had tied it securely, ready for the journey back home.

Jack had let his brother go home for the midday meal, and had brought the load across the paddocks to the front yard himself. He had no particular desire to go inside for dinner, considering the cold, indifferent treatment that always waited for him, so he elected to stay in the yard and unload the timber. The horse stood obediently still, just as it always did when waiting for the driver to move him out, and Jack began to untie the ropes that held the poles safely on the back of the wagon. He had unloaded several pieces before the snake slithered across the yard. It went nowhere near the young workman, but both the horse and the dog saw it, and the ruckus that followed caused the horse to pull back, unsettling the wagon, and the load on the back.

Jack was totally unprepared for the avalanche of logs that tumbled in a mass from the back of the vehicle, and he didn't have time to jump out of the way. Before he could prevent anything from happening, Jack found himself lying under twenty heavy logs, and though he was conscious, he felt severe pain in his leg and arms.

There really was only one option. Neither of his arms would work, and he couldn't lift any of the logs off his body. He would have to call Christine for help. As he opened his mouth to yell, he wondered if she would bother to come.

Christine had heard the noise of the logs tumbling to the ground, but she didn't think it of any account. In the back of her mind she knew that Jack had his brother, Jimmy, with him, and that they had been unloading logs from the back of the wagon the past few days. It never occurred to her that the noise was anything out of the ordinary.

Neither did she hear the frail plea for assistance. She did not know that her husband was seriously injured, lying trapped not twenty yards from the kitchen window. She thought she had heard the dog setting up a bark, and half expected Jack to walk in for dinner. But when he didn't appear, she didn't concern herself. He often elected not to come in, and he had stopped apologising for his absence. And so she went about the work of preparing apricots for preserving, unaware that Jack was still hoping that his voice would be heard.

In his heart, Jack knew that his voice was weak, and that Christine probably wouldn't have heard him, but he was battling with the thought that she had heard the first time, and she had deliberately chosen to ignore his plight.

Every time he formed a new cry, he knew that he couldn't put any strength behind it, because of the sharp pain that caught in his side every time he tried.

He had little to do but to pray that she would come outside for some reason, and that she would choose to look his way. Sadly, he realised that she wouldn't miss him if he didn't return home for dinner or tea. They had become used to the indifference and fractured communication, and too late, Jack began to regret that he had not tried harder to establish some routine at least, that she would miss him.

There was possibly a good hour of agony, both physical and mental before any hope of relief came. Jack knew that he had probably broken a leg and at least one arm. He was engulfed with pain, but no unconsciousness came to spare him the suffering.

Christine had cut and pitted a whole bucket of apricots, and had filled a number of preserving jars with the fruit. Mechanically she decided to go out to the tree and pick more, since there were several jars not yet filled. She had walked out the front without lifting her eyes to see the disaster across the yard, and had been picking fruit for nearly five minutes before an alarm began to ring in her mind.

Suddenly she became aware of the fact that the horse was impatiently snorting, and that the dog was restless. It was more a reflex action of the past that caused her to sense that something was wrong. She put the bucket down, and moved back around the house to assure herself that she was not imagining things.

When she finally saw the pile of fallen logs, the blood ran from her face, and old feelings of fear began to emerge.

'Jack!' she called out, breaking into a run. 'Jack!'

'I'm here!' His answer was feeble, but she heard him.

'Oh, Lord!' Christine was shocked, and more emotion flowed through her being than she had felt in a long time. 'What am I going to do? Jack, what should I do?'

She moved to the pile of logs and began to try to lift the first one she touched, but movement of the heap brought renewed spasms of pain to Jack's whole body.

'Stop!' he groaned. 'Don't!'

'What should I do?' Christine sounded frantic. 'I don't know what to do!'

'Go and get help!' It took all his strength to give the directive, and he hoped that she would have the presence of mind to go as quickly as possible.

Christine didn't think to unhitch the horse and ride, and Jack did not suggest it. Mindlessly, she broke out across the paddocks, running towards the neighbouring farm of her parents-in-law, all the time fighting back the waves of panic that threatened to overcome her.

In all the time she had been back from England, she had not allowed any emotion to move in her. She had become numb to any kind of feeling, and yet now, when faced with this accident, her guard was let down and dread, mixed with other unidentified emotions, coursed through her being.

It was at least a mile and a half to the Browning property, even though she had taken the direct route across paddocks and fences, and by the time she had reached the front doorstep, she was breathing hard, her lungs tortured as the breath rasped in and out.

'Help! Help!' she called out, banging desperately on the wooden door. 'Mrs Browning, help!'

Elizabeth was quick to the door, at once remembering the day that Jack had brought news of Pete's death.

'Jack?' She breathed her fear in that one-worded question.

'Can Mr Browning come quickly? Jack's had an accident!'

This was all Christine was able to get out before the anxious mother let out a loud cry of terror.

'Not Jack! Not him too!' She pushed passed the exhausted girl, racing without thought across to where she knew her children were busy in the yard. 'Get your father, quick,' she ordered. 'Jack's had an accident. Quick, I say.'

Obviously the memory of Pete's untimely death was fresh in the minds of the whole family as two of the younger children immediately began to cry, on seeing their mother's distress. The eldest in the group present, a fifteen-year-old, began to run out towards where his father and older brother were working.

'No, Tom!' Elizabeth called. 'You stay and hitch up the horse for me. Annabelle, you go and get your father!' She addressed this order to the next eldest, a fourteen-year-old.

Christine watched the Browning children work to comfort their mother, and to prepare to leave, but she stood away at a distance, and none of them seemed to be aware of her. She didn't have enough mental energy to perceive the anger her mother-in-law was feeling towards her. She could just as easily shut that out as anything else that had come her way.

And so she observed everything, while still recovering her breath, until Clem Browning, his two sons, Tom and Jimmy, and his wife set out in their wagon at a fast pace. They didn't even come back to her and ask if she wanted to ride with them, but left her to walk back in the direction she'd come. A daze settled over her as she stumbled on.

There were many strong feelings pushing up from underneath, but many months of denying them gave her enough power to prevent any of them from overwhelming her. She wondered several times what it would be like to break down and weep and she wondered whether she would feel better or not.

What Clem and Elizabeth Browning had done in ignoring her, should have hurt her greatly, but she simply brushed it aside. *They all think I'm a tramp*, she thought to herself. *That's the way someone like me is treated. I don't deserve anything better anyway.*

She walked slowly now, not really wanting to go back home. There was the possibility that the Brownings would be too late to save their son, and then it would be her fault. If Jack died, she would be responsible for all the pain and trauma that she had brought into the family.

Then she began to think about how she would feel if Jack died. Somewhere in her dark past, she recalled that she had been overwhelmed with grief when Pete had died, and then Julianne. But that kind of reaction was impossible for her now. Crying and mourning was no longer a permissible reaction, and she had almost learned to scorn those who used it, labelling them as weak and unable to stand up for themselves.

'If Jack dies, then I will be alone,' she muttered to herself. 'They will take the farm away from me, and I won't have anywhere to go. Nobody else cares whether I live or die. At least Jack has looked after me these last months.'

This admission cost Christine a lot, and it also brought with it a moment's regret. She had not allowed Jack the comfort of any positive response before, but now she realised that he had given her something; something which she would lose if he died. It crossed her mind to pray that he would live, but just as quickly, she dismissed prayers as a tool for the weak-minded. There was no God who cared – at least, not for her.

It took Christine three times as long to return home as it had taken her to get to the Brownings, and when she finally approached the front yard, she was filled with anxiety. She wanted to go into her own kitchen and sit down to think, but she saw the Brownings' wagon still in the front yard, and she knew that they must be inside with her husband.

The logs had been lifted aside and were strewn carelessly about, away from where they had pinned Jack. Their horse was no longer hitched to the wagon, and Christine guessed that perhaps they had sent someone to Brinsford to get the doctor.

But that didn't mean anything. They had sent for Doctor Michaels when Pete had died. He came even though it was too late. Was Jack dead, or was he alive? This was a question to which Christine found she wanted the answer, and so she determined to go inside the house to find out for sure.

Tentatively, she walked up the two front steps on to the veranda and lifted the latch on the front door. She didn't know what she was expecting to find, but what came was a surprise.

'Why did you do this to him?' Elizabeth launched out at her the moment she recognised who was at the door. 'You should have left him alone, Christine Shore. You have destroyed our son's life.'

'Is he dead?' Christine asked straight out, her face showing no emotion.

'He could have been,' Elizabeth's voice verged on hysterical. 'You just left him there under those logs without trying to help at all.'

Christine could have offered a defence, but she didn't think it was worth it. They all hated her anyway. Nothing was going to change that fact.

'See!' Elizabeth screamed at her husband. 'She doesn't

even care! No emotion whatsoever! You are a cold-hearted creature, Christine Shore, and it was a dark day that Jack ever thought of marrying you.'

'That's enough now,' Clem interceded. 'There's nothing can be gained by speaking so.'

'She doesn't even deserve to be here,' Elizabeth would not be placated. 'I want her out!'

'Well, we had better see what Jack thinks, first,' Clem bought some time. 'You'd better go on in and talk with him,' Clem indicated the bedroom door to his daughter-in-law.

'He won't want to talk to me,' Christine panicked and backed away. 'Is he conscious anyway?'

'He's conscious, and he did ask us to send you in when you arrived.' Clem was far more calm about the situation than his wife, and he seemed resolved to do his duty this far, though Christine sensed that he was probably just as upset as Elizabeth.

'Go along in now,' he pushed her. 'Whatever Jack wants is what we will do.'

Christine challenged the murderous look in the older woman's eyes, holding her gaze defiantly. Almost as if it was just to get at her, Christine brushed past Elizabeth and went into the room that Jack had occupied on his own ever since the children had been taken.

The curtains were drawn, and the room had a dark, grim atmosphere about it. Christine hated the sense of sickness that hit her as she entered. Jack was lying on top of the bed, fully clothed, his boots still on, a spare blanket thrown over him to keep him warm. His eyes were closed, but she knew that he was conscious.

'I need you to help me, Christine.' She was surprised to hear his voice, clear but full of pain.

'I can't help you, Jack. You'll need the doctor first, and then it's best for your mother to help you.'

'No! I need you. You are my wife. I want you to help me.' His voice was strained, but his intent was plain. He meant to have his way in this.

'I don't even know what's wrong with you, Jack. How can I help?'

'I don't need a doctor to tell me what's wrong,' he countered. 'I've broken some bones, and I can't manage on my own at the moment. I can't move, I can't do anything.'

'But, Jack ...'

'Promise me, Christine,' he urged. 'I have got to know that you will not run away. Promise me you will stay and look after me.'

Christine wanted above all to run away. She didn't know what looking after him would entail, but she knew just how his mother would respond to such an idea. She struggled with several excuses, trying to find one that he would not be able to demolish, but they all seemed lame, especially when she considered that she would have absolutely no place to go if she didn't stay to nurse him.

'When Doctor Michaels comes, you come back in and hear from him what it is you must do.' Jack saw her hesitation as a weakening of will.

'But you don't need me, Jack. You have your mother and your sisters and brothers. They are all capable, and love you better than I do.'

'I know that's true,' Jack sighed, 'but the thing is, you don't have anybody who loves you as well as I do, and I can't look after you if you go away.'

Christine turned and fled from the room, just to get away from the meaning of what Jack had said. She wanted to erase the words from her mind. She didn't want to allow them for a single moment to penetrate her thinking, as she was convinced it couldn't be true.

Nobody loved her; she was dirty, shameful and disgraced. And she wouldn't let anybody lie to her, or lure her into believing that it might ever be possible.

'All right, I'll stay,' she murmured to herself, once outside, 'but only because his mother has enough to do with all the rest of her brood.'

CHAPTER 10

Doctor Michaels had eventually come, some seven hours later, long after the sun had gone from the sky. There was some tension when he asked who was going to assist in the procedure that needed to be done. Elizabeth instantly offered, almost as certainly as Christine declined. It would have worked out easily if Jack had not insisted that it be his wife, and not his mother. Christine saw the resentment on her mother-in-law's face, and would just as happily have given way, but the doctor seemed to have chosen to ignore the family tension, and he urged Christine to follow him.

The good doctor must have wondered at the young wife's aversion to her husband. Christine could not watch as the physician cut Jack's clothes away, leaving him virtually naked. It was not until he had covered him with a blanket again that she would consent to watch any further procedure. Her stomach lurched as she witnessed the doctor's attempts to re-align a bone in Jack's arm. He yelled and writhed in agony, and Christine almost wished that he would just pass out, but he didn't. By the time they had finished, Jack had his right arm set in two splints and bandaged firmly. The doctor had elected to bandage his left arm to his chest to prevent any movement that would upset the broken collar-bone, and he had splinted the patient's lower left leg.

'You need to thank the Lord that the break in your leg is only a simple fracture. It could have been far worse, my boy.'

Christine had no wish to thank the Lord for anything at all. This accident was simply further evidence of the fact that He cared nothing for her.

Before the doctor left, he made a list of instructions for Christine to follow with regard to administering a pain-killing powder, and the way she needed to care for one so incapacitated. She accepted the directions about the laudanum without question, but when the doctor began to talk about normal daily functions that would have been no trouble to any healthy person, but to an invalid like Jack were a major task, Christine began to feel panic rising.

'I can't do this,' she spoke quickly to the doctor. 'I can't do it!'

'Not on your own, Mrs Browning,' he spoke kindly; he was the first person who had ever referred to her by this official title. 'One of your relatives will have to help you turn your husband. Perhaps you could arrange for one of them to come by morning and night to help with the things you can't do.'

'But what about ...' Christine felt like gagging at the thought of keeping Jack clean, and even at feeding him his meals.

'There isn't anything else to be done that you cannot manage on your own,' the doctor carefully reassured her. 'It may take four or five months before your husband is completely independent of you, but I have every hope that he will be able to function fairly normally by then.'

There was nothing left for her to say. Jack was listening to the exchange, though he was somewhat groggy from the powder he had been given. Still, Christine didn't want to risk expressing her fears in front of him. It wasn't that she was afraid that she might hurt him, because she had told herself over and over that she didn't care if she did. It was more that she didn't want him to know how inadequate she really felt.

And now there was the business of facing his parents. How was she going to convince them that she had the right to look after Jack, as his wife, when she hadn't yet even convinced herself that that was what she really wanted to do? But once again, the doctor seemed oblivious to the family breakdown, and he simply announced what he expected would be a suitable solution to the problem. Clem nodded in apparent understanding, and assured Doctor Michaels that he would arrange for either Colin Shore or one of his own boys to help Christine out with the heavy lifting.

Elizabeth made no more biting comments or accusations, but then neither did she make any comforting remarks. Her anger was palpable. It was close to two in the morning by the time Christine was left alone in her kitchen. By this time she was exhausted both physically and emotionally. With a weary heart she fell on her makeshift mattress on the floor, and hoped that sleep would come to block out the many troubling thoughts resulting from the day's events.

Christine was struggling badly. She had woken up at her normal time, her mind foggy from lack of sleep, yet she was determined to get up to face her duty. She didn't bother to check on Jack initially. She needed more time to talk herself into facing that challenge. Finally, she had some porridge ready and a cup of tea for his breakfast. Taking a deep breath to fortify her courage, she carried the tray to the bedroom.

But once inside, her resolve crumbled. Jack was awake, and though she could see he was tangled and uncomfortable, he did not ask for help.

He only had one good leg with which to manoeuvre himself, and each time he had tried to change positions, he had caused himself more pain. From his night-time attempts at making himself comfortable, he had lost his blankets, and had been unable to retrieve them.

'I'm sorry, Christine,' Jack eventually spoke. 'I didn't want to call you in, but I was getting quite cold.' He didn't actually have to ask. She could see what it was that he needed. Though she didn't want to look, she felt that she could at least cover him up, so with eyes averted, she hurriedly gathered up the stray bedding and threw it haphazardly over the patient.

She had become used to silence between them, and so she didn't bother to talk at all, as she placed the breakfast tray on the bed beside him. She turned to exit the room, wanting to get away as soon as possible, but was arrested by his voice again.

'I can't eat this on my own, Christine,' Jack sounded frustrated. 'I am all tied up like a pig for slaughter. You're going to have to feed me!'

Christine had known this all along, but had chosen to ignore it, foolishly thinking that the matter would take care of itself, but now he was refusing to let her ignore it any longer.

'Please!' Jack added this with as much gentleness as he could muster. 'I know it's hard for you, but there are other things we are going to have to do this morning that aren't going to be any more pleasant. This is one of the easy tasks.'

'I can't!' Christine shook her head and ran from the room, across the kitchen and out the front door. When she broke into the fresh morning air she was dry-retching.

The whole incident had upset her totally. 'I can't do it,' she explained to the curious dog. 'You don't understand. It's just impossible.'

And these were the sorts of panicky excuses that she repeated to herself the whole time as she walked towards the manse. She was desperate now. Before the accident, she would have denied herself anything. It didn't matter to her whether she lived or died, but to see Jack so totally vulnerable and at her mercy brought back to life the dormant compassion that had once been part of her nature. She simply couldn't let him lie there and starve, denying him even the most basic comforts. She could no longer turn her back on Jack's needs, and believing that she couldn't meet them herself, she set out in search of someone who could.

'Christine!' Kate was truly surprised to see the young woman at her door, and so early in the morning. 'What's the matter? Is everything all right?'

'Jack's had an accident!' She told her yesterday's news with ease. 'I need your help!'

'Oh, goodness!' Kate was alarmed. 'Is it serious? I shall send John for the doctor straight away.'

'No! No!' Christine objected. 'The doctor came yesterday. Jack has broken some bones and he's helpless. I can't look after him. They told me I could, but I can't.'

'Come along.' Kate couldn't see the point in wasting time talking when there was an emergency. Quickly, she gave directions to her housekeeper, and told John about what had happened. It only took five minutes for the two ladies to be back on the road.

'Tell me what happened,' Kate urged gently.

'A load of wood fell on Jack, from the back of the wagon. The doctor has splinted his right arm and left leg, and has bandaged his left arm to his side.'

'Why?' Kate sounded horrified.

'Apparently, he's broken his collar-bone and a rib as well.' Christine repeated the list mechanically, devoid of any emotion.

'Is he going to be all right?' Kate sounded afraid that he might not be.

'The doctor says he will,' Christine shrugged.

'Christine,' Kate began, tentatively. 'You don't seem to be very upset. How do you feel about what's happened?'

'Feel?' Christine sounded surprised. 'I don't feel anything.'

'Why did you come for me, then?' Kate knew that there must be more to it than that, and though she had her own ideas, she wanted Christine herself to tell her.

'I can't look after Jack, that's all,' Christine tried to brush it aside.

'Doesn't Jack want you there?' Kate asked, surmising that this was the case, and that the old neglect had resurfaced. 'Is your husband still treating you badly?'

'No!' Christine answered slowly. 'He's treated me just like any man who has a tart for a wife.'

'Christine!' Kate was annoyed at her. 'That's not the truth, and you know it. Jack might have thought that at first, before he knew about ...'

'I don't want to discuss that,' Christine cut her off. 'I just need your help. That's all.'

Kate sighed, frustrated at the way she couldn't seem to break through the wall around this girl.

'What is it the doctor wants you to do, that you can't manage?' She decided to go back to the immediate problem.

Christine didn't want to talk about that either, and was silent for a long time.

'Christine,' Kate pressed. 'What is it?'

'He would be better off with his mother,' Christine finally burst out. 'I don't know why they all insisted that I do it.'

'Who's they? Who insisted?'

'Jack!' Christine spat out the name.

'And what is it that he expects you to do?' Kate persisted.

'Can't you just help me?' Christine pleaded, almost whining. 'I can't face all of that.'

'What? What is it that is so bad?' Kate's voice had risen in anger. 'You'd better tell me, Christine, or I shall turn around and not go another step with you.'

'You'll think I'm a lazy and selfish hussy.'

'Are you? Is that what all this is about? You being selfish and lazy?'

'No!' Christine was defensive. 'I just can't face him like this.'

'Like what?' Kate was trying to sound patient in her efforts to extract this information.

'He's naked and helpless. They want me to feed him, and wash him and help him with the necessary.' She finally blurted it out. 'I feel ill every time I look at him. I just can't do it.'

'Is it because of what happened in England, that you feel this way?' Kate didn't really understand, but she was trying.

'You couldn't possibly know what terrors it gives me, seeing him like this. I just want to vomit over and over.'

'But has Jack ever done anything to you to hurt you in this way?'

'That's not the point. He's a man, and that's what men do!'

'Not all men, Christine. In fact, I'd venture to say that it's very few men who would have the depravity of mind to behave the way that Emily's brother did.'

'I don't want to think about it any more. I just want to forget that it ever happened.'

'But you can't?'

'Every time I think about Jack as a man, I see that awful earl leering at me. He stole everything from me, Kate. Everything!'

'But Jack didn't have anything to do with that,' she tried to point out.

'He's still a man!' Christine argued, as if this should be damning evidence.

Kate sighed again, feeling as if she was stuck in a vicious circle. 'There's only one way to break out of this, that I can see,' Kate eventually felt she could comment.

'If his mother could do the nursing, that would help.' Christine felt that she had finally won the issue.

'No! That would only be a temporary solution, Christine. We need something more permanent.'

'Like what?' Christine didn't dare sound hopeful. Suspicion was far safer.

'You need to forgive.'

'Forgive!' Christine exploded. 'Forgive who? That monster, Earl Wallace? Forgive him? Not in a million years. I couldn't. I don't want to! I hate him, and I like hating him. He stole my innocence and my life. I want to make him pay.'

'And you think that this bitterness is really hurting him?' Kate asked, stern in her approach. 'Do you think that he really cares if you love or hate him? He probably doesn't even remember who you are by now.'

'Of course he would remember!' Christine scoffed. 'There isn't a day gone by that I don't relive that nightmare.'

'Emily told me that, after you left, she met several former house staff who had suffered a similar attack like you did. Two of them have small children as a result. Her brother does not even know their names, and he didn't care when Emily faced him with the prospect of illegitimate children. Did you know that Emily left the inheritance from her mother to house those women and their children?'

Christine remained silent. She didn't want to know about this at all.

'Your hatred and bitterness doesn't go any further than your own life and those immediately around you. In fact, Charles Wallace has not only succeeded in destroying you, he is destroying Jack, and your mother and brother and Emily. Only you can put a stop to it!'

'I can't!' Christine turned an agonised face to her counsellor. 'It's too hard. I can't even think of not hating him.'

'But what about Jack? You hate him too, don't you?'

'I have to. It's part of me now.'

'But it doesn't have to be, Christine. You could forgive Jack. He's apologised for all of those things he did before. He's asked you to forgive him for what happened with the Booth girl. You could at least start by forgiving Jack.'

'I wouldn't even know how to start, Kate.'

'You could start by asking the God of forgiveness to forgive you your hatred and anger, and then ask him to give you the gift of forgiveness.'

'There is no God!' Christine was adamant.

'What are you saying?' Kate sounded alarmed.

'If there were a God, He would have protected me. He wouldn't have allowed all those dreadful things to happen.'

'This is going to be a hard one, Christine,' Kate sounded sad. 'I don't have any answers to that at all.'

'There, you see,' Christine sounded triumphant. 'If there is a God, he sits up in heaven and doesn't care what happens to us down here.'

'But He does care,' Kate argued, tears in her eyes. 'He cares so much about you.'

'You'd have to say that! You're a minister's wife.'

'You've become so hard, Christine,' Kate spoke sadly. 'I know that it's the pain that has driven you this way, but I don't know how to get through to you. God wants to heal the pain, but He can't when you won't let Him.'

'I don't believe you.'

'Do you have any other options?' Kate fired back. 'Couldn't you at least give Him a chance?'

'Open myself, and give Him the chance to let me down? No thanks! That's too big a risk.'

'I can't help you, Christine,' Kate drew the horse in to a standstill. 'You'll have to go on home to your responsibilities on your own. There isn't anything I can do.'

'You have to,' Christine insisted.

'I don't have to, Christine. Jack would not want a strange woman tending to his physical needs. He would be thoroughly humiliated.'

'But what about me?' Christine pleaded.

'Well, it seems that it's as you said. You are selfish.' Kate delivered this as firmly as she could. 'There is only one thing I can do to help, and you don't want to believe me.'

'You want me to forgive, when I don't want to.'

'Look! I can understand how hard it is. I struggled with this issue myself before I was married. But you can at least make a step in the right direction. You aren't going to be completely well in one prayer. The whole process of forgiveness is a journey.'

Kate was shooting her last ammunition. There was nothing left after this.

'What if God isn't there, and He doesn't answer me?' Christine was weakening.

'Then I will pack up the manse, and John will become a travelling salesman. Christine, our whole life is dedicated to this one hope. God is there, and He does care. Can't you at least try?'

CHAPTER 11

Jack had been angry and frustrated when Christine had left him so suddenly. Then as time wore on, he became afraid, not so much for himself in his helpless state, as for her. He had been trying so hard to understand how she must be feeling, and why she behaved the way she did, and yet he still felt as much an outsider as ever.

An hour and a half had passed with him praying more for his wife than himself, before his next oldest brother, Jimmy, arrived. Jack didn't really want to discuss with the seventeen-year-old about his private life, and he made evasive excuses as to why he had been left with his breakfast uneaten, and his needs unmet. Still, the younger brother seemed willing enough to allow Jack his private thoughts, and he just did what Jack suggested he do.

By the time Christine returned, sheepishly, to the house, Jack had been fed and tended for the morning. Christine was both glad and ashamed to realise that it had all been done.

'I'm sorry, Jack.' She sounded more repentant that she had ever in the whole time of their stormy marriage.

'Can't we talk about this, Christine,' Jack asked kindly. 'I haven't pressed you before, but I realised yesterday, when I was trapped beneath those logs, that perhaps I should have.'

If Jack had said this to her just two hours earlier, she would have stormed out of the house, as had been her practice, but she had allowed the minister's wife to pray with her. She had taken a chance, and some advice, and she was bound to act on it now.

'Mrs Laslett says that I should forgive you.'

'I wish you would,' Jack sounded hopeful. 'I was a selfish, unfeeling clod to say the things I said to you. You don't know how much I regret it now.'

'You didn't say anything that wasn't true,' Christine spoke resignedly. 'I was all those things you said.'

'Don't say that to me now,' Jack sounded distressed. 'Colin told me that you were attacked. You didn't seduce the man, did you?'

'No!' Christine answered, her gaze turned down.

'You didn't want him to touch you, did you?'

'No!'

'Then you weren't any of those things I said. You were a victim!'

'I feel like it was my fault. I feel dirty and unclean.'

'Because of what he did to you.'

'It doesn't matter any more. It happened. I am what I am. Nothing can change that now.'

'That's not what the reverend said to me.'

'He would! I can't see that God could possibly be interested in me or my life. I'm only sorry that I dragged you into this. I didn't mean to make you suffer as well.'

'Then you do forgive me?' Jack asked, searching her face for eye contact.

'I'm trying to.' She still couldn't bring herself to meet his gaze.

'Don't you believe that I'm sorry for what I did?' he pushed gently.

'Yes! I believe that.'

'Then what is it that's so difficult?'

'You're a man, Jack! I don't trust you because you're a man!' Christine revealed the truth about the core of her fear. 'How can I trust you?' she asked miserably.

'I'm not like that, Christine, I'm not!' Jack seemed desperate to establish the truth.

'What about Miss Booth?' She dropped the question, and even though her tone was subdued, it had the effect of halting Jack in his testimony of his character.

'You're right!' he slowly conceded. 'There is a part of me that gave in to temptation, but I would never have attacked her against her will,' he hurried on. 'I wouldn't have then, and I won't now.'

'Especially not now!' Christine almost allowed a smile as she indicated all of the bandages and splints.

Jack saw a small glimmer of hope and took heart in it. 'You see! There is good that can come out of this accident.'

'What do you mean?' she asked, puzzled.

'I'm quite unable to be a threat to you for a long time. Maybe you can feel safe to talk, now that you can see I can't hurt you.'

'I have to be honest with you, Jack,' Christine launched into the speech Kate had advised.

'I don't mind,' he encouraged.

'I ... I'm afraid ... no. I feel revolted by touching you.'

'I know that!' He seemed unruffled.

'I don't know how to nurse you. It all seems too hard to face.'

'If you want me to, I'll send for my mother. But I don't want her here. I want you here. I don't want you to be afraid of me, and I'll do whatever it takes to help you learn to trust me.'

'I think you're too good for me, Jack Browning. I don't feel that I'm worth the effort. I have a feeling that your mother thinks the same way.'

'This is our life, Christine. Our marriage. If it's going to ever work out, it'll be because we have worked together on it. I won't force you to do the nursing, if you don't want to. But I want you to stay here with me. Please!'

'You could have had so much more, Jack. Someone so much better!'

'You've got it all round the wrong way,' he contradicted. 'I was the one who sinned. You were a victim of sin. I'm the one who doesn't deserve you.'

'Mrs Laslett says I have sinned too.'

'How? What have you done?'

'I've hated you, and that other man. I've been self-centred and uncaring.'

'But you had an excuse.'

'Mrs Laslett says I've had a reason, but not an excuse. Let me feel the remorse for my own wrong doing, Jack. I need to.'

'Only if you will let it go. But I know you: you will just let guilt grow on you.'

Jack felt a measure of satisfaction at having actually conducted a reasonable conversation with Christine. Sure, she was negative and still seemed hard, but she had talked. It was something, and when the effects of his medicine wore off, and the dull, throbbing pain began to increase, he tried to concentrate on things he could say the next time she gave him opportunity.

Christine still felt nothing. She came away from the conversation just as numb as when she had begun. Kate Laslett had challenged her that she needed to break down the walls about her emotions, but Christine had no idea how such a feat could be accomplished. She was willing to grant the fact that Jack had been pleased, despite her pessimism, but was not quite ready to acknowledge that God had had any hand in it at all. She avoided the bedroom for the rest of the day, except to take in his dinner.

She had cut slices of mutton and placed them between large slabs of bread with some tomato chutney. To make it easier, she cut the sandwiches into small bite-size pieces, so all she had to do was hold them close for him to take with his mouth. She tried not to think about how close she was and hurried away once he'd finished eating his midday meal.

In the evening, her brother, Colin, arrived. Christine knew he was going to come sooner or later, but she didn't feel ready to face him. She had a tea-tray ready for Jack, and left it on the table.

'I need to get out for a while,' she excused herself to her brother. 'Will you help Jack eat his tea?' She didn't wait for Colin to answer, but went swiftly outside and away from the house.

Colin felt hurt by his sister's blatant rejection of him, and he blamed himself over and over again for the change in her personality.

'You've really made a mess of yourself, haven't you?' Colin greeted Jack, a little surprised to see just how badly injured his brother-in-law was. 'I get the honour of serving your tea. Hope you don't mind.'

'I don't mind,' Jack spoke through his pain. 'I just hope you have some of the laudanum there. The last lot has worn off.'

'I guess that must be what is in this glass,' Colin surmised. 'How are you and Christine getting along? Any better?'

'Not much!' Jack didn't feel like friendly conversation, though he didn't want to offend his visitor.

'Will things ever improve?' Colin asked, as he held up the glass to Jack's lips for him to drink the liquid.

'I can only pray. The minister's wife had a long talk with her this morning. She was just a little more open afterwards. Perhaps it's a good sign.'

'She hasn't forgiven me yet,' Colin stated matter-of-factly.

'I think she has,' Jack contradicted. 'It's just that she is finding it hard to be open with anybody any more. I think she is afraid that we won't forgive her.'

'There's nothing to forgive,' Colin spoke firmly. 'If anything, I still have to forgive myself. I know that Emily feels the same way. She has taken this rift really hard. She feels as if it's all her fault because it was her brother.'

'Col, just the thought of another man touching Christine makes my blood boil.' Jack's heightened emotions brought the throbbing pain an extra edge, and yet he could not calm himself down from the way he felt. 'I feel so useless, especially now.'

'I know how you feel, Jack.' Colin tried to speak in a soothing way. 'There's nothing we can do. Not here. Not now.'

'Yes, but won't anybody try to bring that man to justice?' Jack turned aggrieved eyes towards his friend, almost as if he were pleading

'I left the policeman all the information I knew, Jack. And Emily tracked down some other victims of his violence. There is nothing more we can do when faced with a man of such power.'

It was a struggle for Jack to get the food down, but he tried because Colin kept bringing the fork to his mouth. He didn't want to eat when he thought about the crime against Christine. He wanted to act. But Colin was right. There was nothing more either of them could do, except try to love Christine through these dark times.

***

Christine gave herself a mental pat on the back. She had managed to nurse her husband for four days without crumbling. Admittedly, she gave Jack's other visitors plenty of opportunity to help, thereby avoiding unnecessary contact with him.

But there was one job she had been ignoring, and the time had come that she must face it, despite the knots of fear that tormented her stomach.

'Do you want to call my mother?' Jack asked her, when the subject had come up between them.

In fact, Christine would have done anything to avoid the job of bathing her husband. However, Elizabeth had made some stinging comments, and a stubborn streak in Christine rebelled against what she had said.

'It won't take a week and Jack will be begging for me to come and nurse him properly,' Elizabeth had said, as they had walked away that night, four days ago. Christine had heard this quite clearly, and for once, it had penetrated and hurt. She didn't want her mother-in-law to be right. She wanted to prove that she was quite capable of doing the job properly.

Before all the trauma had happened, Christine had quite admired Elizabeth Browning. But then she didn't really blame her for her current attitude. She knew that she was no prize wife, and that Jack's mother had every right to be disappointed.

Still, on this morning, the question was there. Did she want to give in and call Elizabeth, or was she prepared to face her fears?

'I can do it,' Christine snapped, trying to hide her anxiety behind a harsh façade.

Jack didn't push her any more, but decided to co-operate with whatever she planned to do.

Swallowing back the nausea that would not go away, Christine got several towels and placed them under her patient, helping him to sit up, and then urging him to hold his head over a bowl she placed on his lap. It was hard, but she managed to pour water over his hair, and lather it up with soap, without yielding to the impulse to run away. After pouring some clean, warm water over to rinse the soap away, she made an off-handed comment. 'You need a haircut, Jack Browning.'

'Can you cut hair?' he asked.

'I used to cut Harry's hair often enough, and I think Mum let me cut Colin's once before he got married.'

'I trust you then. One thing's for certain, I can't trim it myself at the moment, can I?'

'Maybe tomorrow,' Christine put him off. 'I haven't finished this bath yet.'

'How are you going?' Jack asked in a sensitive tone, knowing that this was a difficult thing for his wife.

'I'm managing, but I feel like running away.'

Even as the conversation lapsed, Christine was engulfed with waves of panic as she brought the washcloth over Jack's broad and muscled shoulders. Staring wide-eyed at his chest and what was visible of his arms, she seemed mesmerised, and Jack could not fail to notice. He waited patiently for a minute, not wanting to alarm her, but when she didn't move or go on, he began to talk in a low, reassuring tone.

'Do I look like Charles Wallace?' he asked quietly.

'No.' Christine answered in a hypnotic tone.

'Tell me about what you're thinking.' Jack knew he was taking a risk, but he so much wanted to break through the wall.

'I could not believe how strong he was,' Christine spoke as if in a daze. 'He looked weak and puny. Thin-boned and white-skinned. For a few moments, I thought I would be able to fight him off, but he became enraged, like a madman. He hit me over and over, and I tried to get away from him, but he had locked the door, and I couldn't get out. I tried to hit back, and I screamed and screamed for help. But no one came. Eventually, he threw me on the floor, and then I couldn't get him off of me. Then ...'

But as the picture cleared in her mind, Christine couldn't go on. The nausea overcame her, and she began to retch. Letting the washcloth fall, and knocking over the enamel bowl of water, she rushed from the room and from the house. She ran blindly, not knowing or caring where she went, her stomach retching over and over until she finally lost her breakfast. Finally she stumbled and fell down by the creek, near the place she'd gone those weeks before when she'd wanted to die.

'Oh, God,' she moaned. 'Why didn't you stop him? Why did you let him do that to me?'

Jack wanted to yell and shout, and vomit and run after his wife. But he couldn't seem to do any of those things. He was thoroughly wet, now that the wash bowl had been turned over on the bed, but that didn't worry him as much as what Christine was going through. He wished he could get out of his bed and go look for her, but even if he'd been able to manage it, he realised he was hardly dressed to go outside. Once again, he was left with no alternative but to pray, and pray he did – for over an hour.

And it was God he thanked when Kate Laslett called out at the door.

'Come inside,' Jack yelled as loudly as his cracked ribs would allow.

'Jack?' Kate walked through the deserted kitchen, into the bedroom. 'What has happened to you?' she asked, alarmed when she saw his plight.

'Never mind me. Can you go look for Christine? She ran out of here over an hour ago.'

'What happened? I mean, with all this?' Kate had to ask.

'She was trying to overcome her fear of me. I told her that I didn't mind if she fetched my mother, but she wanted to try.'

'And how far did she get?'

'Just the hair, really. Look, I'm really worried about her. She began to speak about what happened, and then it got too much.'

'Let me get you a dry blanket or something, first,' Kate offered. 'You'll catch your death of cold.'

Jack allowed the minister's wife this much, but then urged her to try and find Christine. Kate decided to start looking where they had found Christine last time, and so it didn't take long to find her.

'What happened, honey?' Kate asked, coming up gently beside the young woman.

'I want to cry,' Christine said flatly. 'I just want to cry and cry.'

'Well, why don't you?' Kate asked, innocently.

'I can't! I don't know how any more.'

'Have you asked God to help you?' Kate inquired, knowing full well that Christine would have difficulty with this concept.

'I've tried, but God doesn't understand the way I feel.'

'How do you know?'

'How could He ever understand the humiliation and shame? How could He ever know what it's like to be powerless and at someone else's mercy?'

Kate allowed some moments to pass in silence. She knew she had a word of wisdom to speak, but she didn't want to be presumptuous by speaking quickly and insensitively.

'You were always a keen Bible student, Christine,' Kate began slowly. 'Do you remember when you were young, how you always used to hound my father for answers to your questions?'

'That was another lifetime,' Christine answered sullenly. 'I can hardly remember.'

'You remember the story of Jesus' crucifixion, don't you?' Kate prompted.

'Of course,' Christine answered.

'You used to believe that Jesus was Immanuel, "God with us".'

'I don't see what you're trying to say.' Christine spoke impatiently.

'Perhaps you'll think more about what happened to him now. Remember, he was stripped naked in front of his family and friends, and government officials. They mocked and taunted him. When they nailed him to the cross, he was totally powerless, at the mercy of the Roman soldiers.'

'Yes, but he could have got down if he'd wanted to.'

'Yes, he could have called an army of angels, but he chose not to.'

'So that he could die for our sins,' Christine recited tonelessly, unimpressed by the old Sunday school lesson.

'Don't you see,' Kate sounded exasperated. 'He has experienced every pain and shame that ever came to mankind. He knows your humiliation; he knows your shame; he has grieved over the pain of the world – your hurt and mine. His death and resurrection are the very things that bring us life in the midst of death.'

'I hear what you're saying. I guess it's true. But I still can't feel anything. It's all just a numb void.'

Kate put her hand on Christine's shoulder. 'Then I will pray that God will restore feeling to your emotions; that he will heal that which has been wounded.'

CHAPTER 12

C oming back to face Jack was awful, especially considering she needed to clean up the mess she had made.

'I've messed this up again,' Christine spoke to her husband, the moment she walked through the door. 'I always seem to end up hurting someone.'

Kate, who'd come inside with Christine, noticed that Jack didn't respond, and she looked to him to gauge his reaction. What she saw stunned her. He was leaning back against the pillows she herself had propped up for him before she'd gone out to find Christine, but his face was contorted in a display of sorrowful agony.

'Are you all right, Jack?' the minister's wife asked. 'Are you in pain?'

Christine looked up now, having not dared to when she first came into the room, and she was astonished at the sight of tears running down Jack's face.

'Why are you crying?' Christine asked, somewhat appalled to see a man in tears.

'I can't do anything to help you,' Jack managed to get these words out through his choked up throat. 'I'm stuck here in this bed, and I can see you're hurting, but there isn't anything I can do. Not a thing!'

'Yes, but it's me that's hurting, not you! Why should you cry? I can't even cry.' Christine argued.

'You don't understand,' he blurted out in frustration. 'You are part of me now. When you hurt, I hurt!'

'But Jack, you have hurts enough of your own. I don't want you to have to feel sorry for me as well.' Christine's agitation was building.

'I can't help it,' he cried, and looked distressed at the way his nose was running, and the fact that he was unable to wipe it.

'Do you need a handkerchief?' Kate stated the obvious, and prodded Christine into fulfilling this service. Christine actually felt strange wiping a grown man's nose. She had done it often enough for her niece and nephew before, but this was different.

'Don't cry, Jack,' she begged. 'You make me feel like crying too.'

'Perhaps that's a good thing,' Kate suggested quietly.

'Yes, but if I ever got started, I don't think I could ever stop,' Christine was actually trying to dismiss a lump that had formed in her throat. 'Jack, please!' She wanted to stop him, but he seemed inconsolable. 'Cry for Pete; cry for Julianne; cry for your lost love, but don't cry for me. I'm not worth crying over.'

'But I love you,' he wept. 'If tears could bring you healing, then I won't ever stop.'

'Kate?' Christine looked to the minister's wife, her own eyes shining. 'Can't you stop him?' But Kate had also given in to the feelings that she could not hide.

Deciding to encourage what had started, Kate came around close to Christine, and put a hand on each of her shoulders. 'We prayed that God would help you to cry,' she whispered. 'It might be time.'

Christine had to admit that the tight ball of pain and anger was pushing up into her neck, and that she longed for it to be released somehow, but the whole prospect frightened her as well. What if she were not able to stop?

'I'm scared,' she admitted. 'I'm scared for you, and I'm scared for Jack. What if I lose control?'

'Don't think about us, Christine,' Kate urged. 'We only want what's best for you.'

Christine turned questioning eyes towards her husband, hoping to see some reassurance there, and she saw just that.

'Go on,' Jack encouraged. 'Cry if you need to.'

'Do you want me to pray?' Kate asked. 'Perhaps it would help.'

Christine didn't answer, but indicated her agreement by bowing her head in reverence. With eyes tightly shut, she struggled against the whirl of emotions that seemed to spin around in her chest, eventually attaching to emerging thoughts. Christine became lost in a strange awareness, where Jack and his encouragement and Kate and her prayer were no longer apparent. Quite suddenly, all she could see, hear and think were the memories of that time months ago, when her world had been turned upside-down. She could literally see the leering, lust-distorted face of her attacker, and she could feel the panic, followed closely by a burning rage, and then lastly a deep shame and humiliation. All of these emotions came bursting forth as lava would from an erupting volcano.

It took several minutes for Christine to emerge from her dream-like state to again become aware of her actual surroundings, and when she did she was somewhat disturbed to find she had collapsed on the floor, and was still sobbing uncontrollably.

'It's all right,' Kate soothed, brushing loose strands of hair away from her face. 'It's better this way.'

Christine pulled back suddenly, overcome with self-consciousness. 'I'm sorry, I'm sorry!' She kept saying over and over. 'I didn't mean to put all that on you.'

'It's nothing,' Kate spoke confidently. 'Do you feel better?'

'I feel that was just the beginning. I have so much more in there that I want to get rid of.'

'Then do it. Jack won't mind, will you, Jack?' Kate asked pointedly.

'No!' Jack shook his head, trying to sound confident, not willing to confess that he'd been shaken by the hysterical display. 'It's for the best, really.'

'Maybe later.' Christine brushed them both aside as determinedly as she had the straying tears. 'There's plenty of time later. I need to clean up this mess right now.'

Kate watched a little frustrated as Christine apparently corked up the flood of tears that had miraculously begun. Christine busied herself with picking up the wash bowl and cloth, and muttered under her breath about finding dry bed linen.

'Would it be all right if you help me shift Jack, and we can make the bed again?' Christine asked, intent on changing the focus.

'That's fine, Christine,' Kate tried to sound patient. 'I hope that the pair of us will be strong enough to lift you, Jack.' She included the patient in the conversation.

'Is that it, then?' Jack was not quite as willing to let go the intensity of a few moments before. 'Are you just going to push it all down again?'

'Give me time, Jack,' Christine actually dared to look at him without showing fear. 'I will continue this, but not now.' Even as she spoke, more tears had gathered, and she brushed angrily at them, as if they had come against her will. 'Right now I want to make sure you don't become a victim of pneumonia.'

It was as easy as that to dismiss the breakthrough. Christine became more intent on fixing up the muddle now, so that she didn't have to think about what had just happened.

'Why did she have to retract like that?' Jack was frustrated, and asked this question of Kate, when Christine had taken the linen outside to the wash-tub.

'Didn't you notice?' Kate asked, a smile dancing on her lips.

'Notice what?' Jack was not amused.

'She was so determined to hide the tears that she forgot all about you. About her fear of you, I mean.'

Jack maintained his frown, trying to see the point.

'She put her arms around you quite naturally. She didn't hesitate when it came to helping you into that chair. Has she done that before?' Kate asked, triumphant in her tone.

'Well ... no. I don't recall that she ever has.' Jack's forehead started to relax as he was beginning to see Kate's point.

'Ever has what?' Christine asked as she came back into the room.

'Nothing!' Jack answered guiltily. But in his mind he had to admit that there had been a change. Christine seemed more like the girl he had known in his youth than the bitter woman he'd been married to.

Neither the minister's wife nor Jack dared mention this positive sign to Christine in case she became self-conscious and retreated behind her wall. And it was a good thing, because she would probably have done just that. In the supreme effort to control her emotions, Christine didn't have the mental capacity to guard her outward actions as well as her inner responses. If the other two had only known how hard it was for her not to crumble under the urge to weep, perhaps they wouldn't have looked so satisfied. It was as if a crack had formed in her defences, and she could not stem the flow of tears that pushed constantly. All she could do was make cheerful sounding excuses to be out of the room, each time allowing another course of tears to fall. A little later, Kate excused herself and went home. Christine was glad, as it gave her much more time alone, during which she was able to let out more and more of her anguish, and each time her face contorted, and the sobs rose unchecked.

Jack exercised as much patience as he could muster, but he longed to ask his wife questions. He wanted to know what was going on inside; what she was feeling; what she felt about him. He wanted so much to grow closer to her, and yet he held his peace. She was still too fragile and he feared frightening her away.

'How are you feeling?' he asked the following day.

'How are *you* feeling?' She avoided the question, not wanting to trigger the emotions again.

'Me?' He seemed surprised at her uncharacteristic concern. 'I'm as well as a man can be, all bandaged up like this.'

'Well, there's nothing wrong with your tongue, that's for sure,' Christine set the breakfast tray on the side table, and pulled her chair up close to the bed. 'I hope you're hungry this morning.'

Jack was amazed at her openness, and could only nod. He received the cooked breakfast with as much dignity as he could muster under the circumstances, but he was full of questions. 'Do you think it would be all right if we took this bandage off around my left arm?' he asked hopefully.

'No!' Christine was instantly alarmed. 'You shouldn't! I won't let you. It's only been five days, Jack. You'll cause yourself another injury.'

Jack waited, somewhat disappointed, but not willing to give up. 'Is that the real reason,' he pushed gently, 'or are you still afraid of me?'

Christine turned her face away, but she couldn't let the question pass as she might have done a week ago. 'Perhaps

I am a little afraid,' she admitted, 'but it is still too early. Doctor Michaels would be upset if he found out I had let you do such a thing.'

'What about when I am allowed?' Jack was on a thought now and wanted to follow it through.

'I'll have to face it sooner or later, I guess, but not now. Don't push me too fast, Jack. You have to confess that I am at least trying.'

'Yes! I can see you're trying, and I know it's hard, but I guess I'm just impatient, not to mention frustrated, being confined like this.'

'I'm sorry.' Christine was genuine in her apology. 'I guess you must be chafing to be outside and about the place.'

'Yes! I am.' He paused thoughtfully for a few moments, and then went on: 'I'm also chafing to be able to reach out and touch you.'

Christine drew her head up quickly, panic in her eyes. 'I don't know, Jack,' she spoke breathlessly. 'That seems too much for me at the moment.'

'But you can touch me, now, without the same revulsion you felt before,' he argued. 'You even promised to cut my hair.'

'You're impatient, Jack.' She got up from her seat, and took up the breakfast tray. 'I don't think I can move that fast.' Without giving him another opportunity to respond, she walked out of the room, leaving him to regret his haste.

The next few days passed with some form of routine now established. It was true that Christine found she could wash Jack, and help him move from side to side, adjusting pillows and blankets, without the same nausea that had so often threatened to overwhelm her before.

She marched into the bedroom several days later, a pair of scissors in her hand, and two extra towels. 'Are you ready?' She spoke as if the haircut had been discussed in detail.

'If you are,' Jack responded. He didn't want to push any more. 'You are safe with those things?'

'I might be,' she answered almost playfully. 'On the other hand, I might let them slip if I feel under any pressure.'

'I see!' Jack took the threat in a light-hearted manner, but he also decided to heed the veiled warning. It was hard not saying anything. Jack had begun to enjoy her contact, and wondered every now and again, if it were not actually a fond caress that he felt as she ran her fingers through his long, wavy hair. He had to constantly remind himself that she was performing a duty of personal hygiene, and that she probably had no ulterior motive behind the way she brushed the hair up between her fingers and cut the length away, other than getting the job done.

'Thank you, Christine,' he expressed his gratitude with real depth of feeling. There was a new intensity of tenderness that shone in Jack's eyes, and Christine could not fail to recognise it.

'Why are you doing this?' she asked, trying to sound cross.

'Doing what?' Jack feigned innocence.

'Looking at me like that, as if you ... as if you ...'

'As if I love you?' he asked mischievously.

'You're impossible to understand,' she brushed him aside. 'I don't know if I can return that feeling to you. You shouldn't give so much away. You'll only get hurt!'

'But you do care that I might get hurt?' He knew he had her with this question. 'You do, don't you?'

'I don't want to see that, Jack. There has been too much gone wrong. I don't want any more bad things to happen to you.'

'You are not a bad person, Christine. I can see the beautiful, lively girl you used to be. She is not very far away, and I realise now, I probably loved you even back then. I should have thought about it more then, and maybe … well, maybe things might have been different.'

'Are you sure those logs didn't knock you in the head?' Christine attempted to steer the conversation back to safe ground. 'You sound positively soppy. I'd never have taken you for a romantic dreamer.'

'This is more than a dream, Christine.' Jack was determined. 'I'm beginning to thank God for those logs. Perhaps they have been what has shaken us enough to take a long hard look at the way things really are.'

Christine just shook her head, clicking her tongue in pretend disgust, and retreated from the room and from the emotions she wasn't yet ready to face.

CHAPTER 13

*T*he routine was becoming familiar now, and Christine knew she could expect her eldest brother to assist helping with Jack in some of the more difficult tasks.

Since her encounter with Kate, and the following breakthrough on an emotional level, Christine had found herself on the verge of tears much of the time. She worked doubly hard to hide this from Jack, making her conversations with him short and abruptly cut them off whenever she felt a surge of emotion about to overtake her.

Of course, since he did not know exactly what was happening, this sudden break in communication only frustrated Jack. He had held high hopes that his wife would begin to return to normal, following the violent explosion of pent-up sorrow. But, from his observation, he wondered if perhaps the opposite had been achieved.

But he didn't know that every time she hurried away, she would soon be engulfed in yet another wave of tears, trying without success to push back the memories and pain that she had harboured for the best part of a year, ever since the time that her sister had passed on.

Christine was having to come to grips with the fact that something had broken open that day, a week ago. The wall that had once been there to protect her from further hurt had a breach in it, and now it neither kept new pain out, nor did it keep old pain in.

Somewhere along the line, God had answered someone's prayer, but Christine wasn't sure whether the cure might not have been worse than the disease. Often she shuddered to think just how open she was becoming, and just how vulnerable this actually made her.

She realised that Jack would not be confined, nor would he be ignorant of this vulnerability forever, and that sooner or later, she was going to have to face him and his much expressed desire for intimacy.

But even closer than this horrifying threat was the encroaching problem of the family, both Jack's and her own. Christine knew that she had been cruel and self-seeking in shutting them out, but unlike previous times, she found that she could no longer excuse her behaviour.

She had heard the minister's wife when she'd lectured on the difference between an excuse and a reason, and as much as she didn't really want to admit it, she was becoming more and more convicted that she had, in fact, treated them very badly.

The only other course of thinking available to her was that she would have to take responsibility for her selfish behaviour, and that eventually, she would have to apologise.

The old excuse, that they would never forgive her, was losing more and more merit as each day passed. Christine had never known anyone in her family to bear a grudge for long. She had seen forgiveness encouraged by the minister and often practised by those she had loved in the past.

And now, Colin was due to come in again. Christine was finding it harder to avoid him. Somewhere, deep down in her heart, she longed to have their friendship and the old sibling rivalry restored. Really, the only issue that separated her from most of her former relationships was pride.

It was not easy facing this realisation, but Christine had to admit that reconciliation depended on her and her willingness to allow her family to share her deepest hurts. She knew that in all honesty, none of the reasons she had used to maintain her hermit-like existence were even valid.

The light tap on the outside door was enough to cause new tears to form. Christine brushed angrily at them before getting up to answer the door.

'Colin.' This was as much as she felt able to express without crumbling.

'How's Jack?' Colin didn't seem particularly cheerful either, rather subdued in fact.

'As well as can be expected.' Christine backed away from the doorway as she answered. 'Thanks for coming to help.'

This was the first peace token Christine had found enough courage to offer, and she was surprised at her brother's response. Tears would have come anyway, even if she hadn't seen the shiny glaze in his eyes.

'It's been hard for all of us, Chris.' He spoke, his voice thick with emotion, and Christine instinctively knew that he was referring to the England affair, and not to her husband's injury. Colin continued in the same tone. 'Emily has taken it so hard, blaming herself over and over for what happened.'

Christine wanted to respond; to tell him that she knew it wasn't really Emily's fault, but her throat had tightened, and her lower jaw ached with emotional tension. She couldn't get the words to form in her mouth.

'Won't you see her?' Colin's eyes were glistening with unshed moisture, and he seemed almost to plead with his sister. 'She's been so depressed and I'm worried for her and the baby.'

'Charles?' Christine became alarmed over her two-year-old nephew's welfare, and it was this alarm that seemed to release her vocal chords, allowing her to say just the one word.

Colin shook his head. 'No! It's not Charles. Emily is in the family way again,' he told her without any animation. 'But she hasn't found any joy in the news. She hasn't had any joy since ... you know, since England.'

Christine allowed her tears to flow again unchecked, wiping her eyes and nose, and working only to hold back the sobs that would have been too much to concede.

'Won't you see her, sis?' he pleaded one last time. 'For old times' sake?'

Christine nodded her assent, wiping at another stray teardrop as she did so, but she couldn't get any words out.

'Will you come with me to the great house?' Colin pushed one step farther.

'Oh! No!' Christine was fretful, and once again this strong feeling managed to loosen her voice. 'I'm not ... not ready yet, Col. Please ... don't make me.'

'All right,' he reassured in a gentle tone. 'When Emily is feeling better, I'll bring her out here to see you.'

Nothing further passed between brother and sister, and Christine left the house while Colin went in to see to her husband's needs.

'You seem a bit down,' Colin observed to Jack.

'I'm bored and frustrated,' Jack answered almost crossly.

'Things seem a little better with Christine.' Colin was trying to take hold of the hope implied by the recent exchange.

'Do you think?' Jack seemed surprised. 'I still haven't made much progress, I'm afraid.'

'Oh?' Colin sounded a little concerned.

'Do you think, perhaps, it's just me?' Jack spoke bitterly. 'Maybe I'm fooling myself.'

'How do you mean?' his brother-in-law asked.

'Maybe she won't ever be able to love me, even when she does get better. Perhaps I've cursed the whole marriage from the beginning.'

'I don't quite follow.' Colin sounded genuinely puzzled.

'I agreed that it didn't matter about love. Right from the start I told her I didn't love her, and that I didn't care whether she loved me or not.'

'And now?'

'I can't understand why I didn't see it before! Why didn't I wait for her?' Jack's tone had grown more intense, and Colin could see that he was struggling against the bandages that restrained him.

'I was bewitched by Eunice Booth,' Jack continued, 'and she succeeded in tearing my heart out. I should have just waited for Christine. I should have seen who she really was then. I should have begged her to stay home here in the first place!' Jack was distressed and angry with himself for these apparent failures.

'If my memory serves me correctly, I believe you were only one step short of begging,' Colin allowed just a touch of a smile, hoping to ease his friend's self-recriminations. 'Let me help you stand up for a while,' Colin offered, trying to change the focus of their discussion. Together, the two men struggled against gravity in attempting to set Jack upright, using his good leg to stand on, and supported by Colin on the other side.

'I'm so sick and tired of being in this bed,' Jack expressed his discontent readily. 'I feel as if I'm always on my own, especially lately. Christine doesn't want to stay here for more than is strictly necessary. I had thought she might have been getting better.'

'I think she seems better,' Colin said tentatively.

'Then she must just hate me,' Jack spoke bitterly. 'What an absolute botch I've made of everything!'

'Just give her some more time,' Colin encouraged. 'Surely, if you can love her, she will learn to love you back.'

'Maybe she never will.' Jack seemed determined to make the worst of it.

Colin couldn't swear to anything where his troubled sister was concerned, so he refrained from offering too much, in case it turned out to be false hope. But he did act upon the small olive branch that had been held out to him by his sister.

Even though her recent health had been poor, Emily was immediately bolstered by the news of the opportunity to visit with her beloved estranged sister-in-law. In fact, Colin realised with amazement that a lot of his wife's ailments had been due more to the strain of guilt and broken relationship than from the coming child. It was all he could do to insist that they wait two or three days before returning to the farm.

Christine was not really expecting Emily to come quite so soon, and so when Colin knocked on the door, she was naturally surprised.

'Is everything all right?' she asked. 'Emily and Charles?'

'You said you would see her,' Colin reminded her. He was just a little bit afraid that Christine might have changed her mind.

'Yes!' Christine nodded, at once aware that the emotion that had been frozen in her for so long was now ready to pour out at the slightest provocation.

'Is it all right, then, if she comes inside?' Colin sounded apprehensive, but took courage as he saw his sister nod her agreement. With a thick lump constricting her throat, and that familiar ache in her neck again, Christine watched as her brother walked back towards the carriage. She didn't have the courage to stay and watch. Her eyes were cast down and she was struggling with the urge to run away. The fear of rejection had become a formidable enemy.

Eventually, the sound of footsteps on the veranda floorboards told Christine that it was time to face whatever was to come. The door opened, and she looked up tentatively, hoping desperately on the one hand, and full of fear on the other.

Colin entered, but Christine looked straight past him to search for the expression on Emily's face, the moment she saw her. It was so important to Christine that she see some familiar spark of friendship from the past, as so much had happened that had threatened to destroy totally what they had once shared.

But if she had thought she might see resentment or anger there, one glimpse of Emily's countenance was enough to dispel all those fears. Emily too was searching anxiously, looking for a sign of forgiveness and acceptance. The fracture in their relationship had been a painful and traumatic time for the young mother.

'I'll just go in and check on Jack,' Colin excused himself, leaving the two young women to face each other. For an undefined period of time, the pair stared at one another, verging on tears, neither able to speak.

Eventually, Emily half-spoke, half-sobbed, 'I'm sorry! I'm sorry! I'm sorry.' The tears flowed naturally over this, and Christine wanted so much to hold her friend in an embrace, but she was too shy to initiate it.

'No!' she overrode. 'It was me! I'm sorry, Emily. It was my fault!'

Emily moved forward, shaking her head, as if to discount this confession, moisture flowing unchecked down her cheeks. As if it was the natural thing to do, Christine moved into the arms that she had ached to hold herself, and they both cried unrestrainedly.

'God, help us!' Emily managed to pray. Christine couldn't even nod her agreement.

Colin stood facing Jack. Both of them could hear the exchange in the next room, and Colin could see the tension evident on Jack's face. 'Can't you do something?' Jack hissed through his teeth. 'You can't just leave them like that!'

Colin put his finger up to his mouth, indicating to Jack that he should just wait. He watched the injured man's face, and he knew exactly what he was thinking, and exactly what he would have done, if he had not been restricted. 'It's better that we just sit quietly, mate,' Colin whispered firmly. 'It will all work out somehow.'

'But ...' Jack began, wild-eyed.

'We will only be interfering where we're not wanted. Let them work it through together.'

Jack let out a sigh of pent-up tension, falling unhappily back into his pillows. He might not have loved her when he first came up with the idea of marriage. He might have made some terrible mistakes, but now he just wanted to hold her. If only he could put his arms about her shaking shoulders, he felt that he could show her some of the depth of feeling that had been growing inside his heart.

***

Colin had been right of course. No matter how impulsive Jack wanted to be, the facts remained: Emily and Christine had spent a most productive afternoon, despite the inevitable unsightly red eyes and noses. Colin and Emily had driven away from the farmhouse talking freely in a way that they had not done for months.

Christine had stood on the front veranda and watched the carriage disappear from sight. It was only as she turned back into the house that she noticed how light she actually felt. She was able to identify it easily as the lifting of a burden from her heart and her body.

The minister's wife had talked so much about this happening that Christine didn't need more than a moment to recognise it for what it was, and something else was left in its place as well. She actually felt like smiling. An old negative thought crossed her mind just for an instant, but she had a well of energy which enabled her to brush it away quickly.

'I don't care,' she spoke aloud to herself. 'I don't care if it is a risk. I'm going to smile.'

'I think it's time we had the doctor come and check on you,' she announced happily, as she waltzed into the sick room. 'I'm getting tired of having to do everything for you!'

Jack wanted to make a comment, but he wasn't quite sure where her focus was. He couldn't tell whether she was angry or upset, and he wasn't quite ready to consider that she might even be happy.

'Well! How do you feel?' She seemed impatient. 'Aren't you ready to begin using that arm yet?'

'Of course I'm ready!' he retorted. 'I was ready last week, but you wouldn't let me take this infernal bandage off.'

'That's right!' She smiled at him. 'And I won't now either, not until Doctor Michaels has given his approval.'

'Are you all right, Christine?' Jack was confused by her sudden good humour, and asked the question with sensitivity in his tone, certain that some of the old pain must be somewhere near.

'Yes! I am!' Christine smiled at her husband again, and as she did so, a wave of emotion came and her face crumpled, as her lips quivered and tears formed.

'I am all right, Jack. I didn't think I ever would be again, but I am!'

Jack watched as her words contradicted her facial expression. 'Why the tears?' he finally asked.

'I don't know!' Her words had lost their starch now, and she was blubbering again.

'Christine!' Jack spoke gently. 'Would you come and sit close to me? I can't come to you, but I just want to be close to you.'

It was as he spoke that she realised that she had enough courage to face the dread she usually felt, and she wanted desperately to overcome that panic. She moved around the bed, and climbed on to her side, shuffling herself nearer to Jack than she had ever been in their whole married life, pausing to look into his eyes, hoping she would see something safe.

'It's all right,' he whispered. 'I won't hurt you.'

'I know,' she answered. 'It's only the ghosts of the past that threaten me.'

'Put your head on my shoulder,' he directed, 'if you can.'

There was something akin to anxiety as well as cold fear in the pit of her stomach that Christine refused to yield to. Carefully, not wanting to aggravate any of his injuries, she leaned against the propped-up pillows, allowing her head to lie right next to his.

'What are you thinking?' Jack asked, not wanting to break the sense of peace that enveloped them.

'I'm thinking that you really are a good man, Jack,' Christine conceded, even though she still felt slightly uncomfortable. 'I have treated you very badly. You deserve much better, you know.'

'Don't ...' He turned his head to look into her face, only inches from his own. 'Don't say those things, Christine. God has given you to me, and me to you. I just want to learn to be thankful for that.'

'But what about ... ?'

'About England?' He guessed her apprehensions, and she nodded against his shoulder.

'We can't change the past, the crime against you, and my unfaithfulness to you. I wish we could, but we can't. So, there must be a way through. There must be a way for us to turn our hurts into something strong.'

'What about your mother?' Christine wanted to air all her fears. 'I don't blame her for her opinion of me, but it is what it is.'

'I don't think your mother has much of an opinion of me either,' Jack half-smiled. 'She hasn't said much to either of us since she took the children.'

'They were the only things in my life that meant anything to me,' Christine let the words slip out. 'I wanted to die when Mum took them away.'

Jack tried not to take her words as an attack, though he was very much tempted. 'Do you think I could ever mean anything to you?' he asked carefully. 'Do you think you could ever love me?'

Christine heard his question and understood it fully. The now familiar tears brimmed in her eyes again as she struggled against the lump in her throat.

'When I was just a young girl,' she began her answer, swallowing back her emotion, 'I always used to imagine what it would be like if you were to love me, like Pete loved Julianne. I used to watch the two of them, and I always thought that what they shared as friends, and then as husband and wife, was such a beautiful thing. I did wonder about you, Jack. Many times. I always thought you were handsome, and you always seemed nice.'

She paused her narration and looking into his eyes, she tried to gauge his response to her words.

'I've been thinking about it lately, Jack, and I've realised that, deep down, I've always loved you.'

'I don't quite understand.' He pulled his head away a few inches, surprised by the revelation. 'You were angry at me when I suggested we marry for the children's sake.'

'I know,' she dropped her eyes. 'I was stupid. I guess I was disillusioned from that childhood crush, and I had begun to long for something romantic; some knight in shining armour, to sweep me off my feet. You said you didn't love me, and at the time, the thought of another country seemed so magical and full of promise. If only I could have seen your heart then, and if I'd known what England really held.'

'So you don't hate me any more?' Jack pushed.

'I never hated you, really.' Christine was ashamed that he had thought that. 'I'm just afraid of you.'

'Still?'

'Not so bad as a while ago. I'm getting stronger. See, look how close I am to you, and not panicking.'

'I still can't move,' he pointed out, to see her reaction to the thought.

'We'll have to cross that bridge when we come to it,' Christine was earnest.

Silence fell for a few minutes, Christine involved with her own thoughts, and Jack trying to search for deeper courage.

'Christine!' He finally broke the calm. She lifted her eyes back to meet his. 'Would you let me kiss you?'

Unbidden horror rose in Christine's throat, and she pulled away slightly.

'It's all right,' Jack spoke quickly, trying to reassure her. 'You don't have to. Not if you don't want to.'

'I do!' She spoke firmly. 'Because I know now that I do love you, I want to overcome this stupid fear, but I'm not sure about right now.'

'Just forget I mentioned it,' Jack tried to return to the relaxed conversation they had been sharing. 'It doesn't matter to me.'

'That's a lie, Jack, isn't it?' Christine challenged him. 'It does matter to you!'

He withstood the confrontation by staring unashamedly back. 'I can't lie to you,' he admitted. 'It does matter, but I won't push you. Only when you are ready.'

'What if I'm never ready?' Christine wanted to see the depth of his commitment, and test herself as well.

'Never is a long time.' He looked slightly disappointed. 'But I'd sooner that than losing you altogether.'

'You're too good for me, Jack Browning.' Before she rolled away from him, she searched for a deep surge of courage, and having found it, she placed a gentle kiss on his eyebrow.

CHAPTER 14

When Christine had asked her brother to send for the doctor, he had returned with a message. Doctor Michaels was willing to come, and Colin was willing to pay his fee, but he sent ahead to let the Brownings know that he would not allow the splints to be removed at least until seven weeks from the time of the accident. Christine stalled the visit, naturally not wanting her brother to be paying for an extravagance. Jack had been disappointed at the news, and had struggled with the natural depression that came with the realisation that he was to be confined for at least another three weeks.

Christine recited to herself the many reasons for Jack's ill humour, and in her mind she knew them to be true, but her heart had been returning to normal, and she couldn't help the hurt that would sting her at his short-tempered outbursts. Still, even in spite of this setback, Christine was determined not to return to that place where she had wandered in numbness and darkness for so long.

If it hadn't been for the regular visits from Kate Laslett and her husband, Christine might eventually have succumbed to the temptation to withdraw from the new hurt.

'You have been doing so well,' Kate Laslett had spoken by way of encouragement, after Christine had hesitantly shared her own crushed feelings. 'This is really a good sign, Christine!'

'I don't understand how,' Christine looked mournful. 'It was better before when I didn't care. At least then I was not vulnerable. He could have said anything he liked then and it would not have made a scrap of difference to me.'

'But don't you see?' Kate sounded positively excited. 'If you are feeling pain now, it means your emotions are beginning to work again. Our prayers are being answered.'

'I can't see how that could be good.' Christine remained unconvinced. 'I don't like this feeling, this heartache I feel every time he snaps at me.'

'We both know how hard this must be for Jack.' Kate placed her china teacup back on its saucer. 'He doesn't mean to take it out on you, and he will be sorry for it when he finally does come through. I know you can forgive him. Let the wound heal quickly. Cry when you need to, and let God take the ache from your soul.'

Christine had experienced too much of God's healing already to deny that it was possible. Once again, she recognised that it was entirely up to her, and her own willingness to let things go, rather than storing up a grudge.

The three remaining weeks dragged by with Christine using all her willpower to ignore Jack's grumbling and apparent rejection. During this time, their own struggling relationship was set back quite a distance, but in a way, Christine saw this as giving her more time to adjust to the risk of intimacy.

Finally, Doctor Michaels was sent for and his arrival seemed to boost Jack's spirits momentarily. He must have noticed the difference, but the doctor made no comment about what he observed. Unlike that time he had first attended, the young Mrs Browning hovered about her husband's bed, watching closely, asking many questions, and generally showing that she cared very much how things would turn out for Jack.

However, both husband and wife were discouraged to find that Jack's right hand had very little movement, and he found it very difficult to stand, let alone walk.

'The bones have healed,' the doctor informed them, 'but your muscles have become weak from lack of use. You will need to exercise your limbs frequently, and if your wife could massage some liniment into your muscles, you should regain some use of both arms and leg.'

'Some use?' Jack sounded impatient again.

'You were very lucky, son,' Doctor Michaels ignored his comment. 'I have had cases where I have had to amputate limbs because of bad breaks. You have all your limbs, and you have some work to do. How well you become is up to you and the good Lord.'

'Do you mean to tell me …' Jack began in an explosion of anger, but Christine placed her hand on his arm, and restrained him.

'There is a good chance that my husband will regain full use, isn't there?' she asked calmly, hiding the fear of her own heart.

'There is always a good chance,' Doctor Michaels nodded in agreement. 'I'm not a specialist in this field, you understand. Medical science is making new discoveries all the time, but I only ever read about it from journals sent on odd occasions from England. I am almost as frustrated as you, young man.' He glared seriously at Jack. 'I have read about amazing recoveries through new procedures, but I am too old now to be travelling abroad to learn all about what is happening in my profession. I suppose it is something that we must accept. These things take time and a lot of money. We live a long way from where they are making these advances, and we must learn that God is still our strength and source. Perhaps it will be different some day.'

'God has not let us down so far,' Christine spoke out rather timidly. 'I can see no reason for us to start doubting whether He will see us through now.'

But the physical healing was painfully slow. Christine watched hopefully as Jack applied himself to the exercises that the doctor had recommended, but she was often disappointed whenever he yielded to his frustration, many times directing some form of anger towards her. She didn't let him know how much this hurt her, but it served as a barrier between them, and in one way a protection, when it came to her having to massage the strong-smelling liniment into his arm and leg.

'You know, it's funny,' Kate Laslett commented, one afternoon after Christine had poured out her feelings.

'How can it be funny?' Christine sounded cross at the comment.

'I'm sorry! That's not what I mean,' Kate amended. 'What I'm trying to say is how your situation is almost ironic.'

'I don't understand.'

'You and Jack have both been injured; you emotionally, he physically. And the pair of you have had to stand by and each watch the other go through the painfully slow process of recovery. Your heart and Jack's limbs have taken a similar path when it has come to healing.'

Christine thought about the comment for a while, and tried to draw parallels. 'Do you mean to tell me that it was as frustrating as this, waiting for me to get better?' she finally asked. But even as the question tumbled from her mouth, she knew it must have been as bad, perhaps worse. 'Oh, poor Jack. Poor you!' she exclaimed, suddenly aware of the difficulties that she had caused those around her. 'I guess I was a lot worse than Jack, wasn't I?'

'I don't think your husband begrudges you the time you needed. He understood that there was a lot of pain and fear to be faced.'

'But I should understand his pain and discouragement, too, shouldn't I?'

'If you can find it in your heart,' Kate spoke calmly, as she sipped her tea.

This talk with the minister's wife gave Christine new courage in helping Jack with his recovery. Though she actually found it difficult to voice her gratitude, she wanted to show him how much she appreciated his sticking by her during the difficult times.

Life began to take on new meaning as day followed day. Christine's renewed friendship with Emily provided her with something to look forward to, despite the odd temptation to question the wisdom of being open. There even came a time when she dared ask her sister-in-law how Pete and Julianne were faring.

'They would be fifteen months, now,' Christine commented wistfully.

'Fifteen months and full of mischief,' Emily laughed. 'They are such dear little things, though I wonder where your mother gets the energy to keep up with them. Julianne is far more boisterous than Charles, and I find that his antics alone are enough to keep me quite worn out!'

'Is there a nanny at the great house?' Christine asked, just short of asking if she could take the position.

'Well, we have had our disagreements on this point,' Emily sighed. 'Aunt Vera thinks it scandalous that I have been tending to my son myself, but I watch your mother and I feel as if I want to do things the way she has with Colin and the rest. She managed with the six of you on her own and seems to find no difficulty with the twins. To tell the truth, I'd feel somewhat of a failure if I employed a nanny.'

'Yes, but you weren't brought up to ...'

'Fiddle-faddle,' Emily cut her off. 'I may be Charles' mother; spoiled aristocrat; but Colin is his father, and he is a hardworking man with responsibilities. It has been difficult, I will confess, but I'm determined to give my son a good example, and not teach him to be lazy and idle.'

The conversation hadn't quite gone where Christine had hoped. She had wanted to hear more about the two children she had once begun to see as her own. She had wanted to hear Emily tell her that she was needed, and that she should come for the children at once; but Emily had not read her thoughts, and had almost forgotten that Christine had been the one-time mother of the twins. A depressing silence fell upon the pair, the one dwelling on the regret and pain she felt, and the other wondering what she had said to have caused this slump in spirits.

After Emily had gone, Christine assisted Jack to his feet, and steadied him as he gained his balance. Jack was beginning to walk with the aid of a walking-stick. His left arm was quite useful, his collar-bone having healed nicely, and at least he was able to support some of his own weight while his right leg remained obstinate and weak.

'I'd like to get out,' Jack announced to his wife. 'I'd like to go for a visit with my folks.'

Christine had not been quite prepared for this announcement. She had not been much out of her house, other than to see to the garden, for over two months. She had comforted herself with the progress she had made and had justified her hermit-like existence, citing each step of healing as a good enough reason to have stopped at home. But what she didn't want to admit was that she had begun to see the home as some form of security, particularly with Jack in it. She had no desire to leave the safety of these four walls. Facing her fears here in the familiar surroundings was one thing, but to add the uncertainty of venturing away was like knocking the crutches out from beneath Jack.

'Do you think you could hitch up the horse?' Jack pushed, unaware of her tumultuous thoughts. 'I'm tired of being cooped up in here.'

'I ...' Christine paused for only a few seconds. 'If you are sure that's what you want,' she conceded.

Jack didn't seem to sense her apprehension, and Christine didn't have the nerve to voice her fears, so she went about harnessing the horse and hitching him to the wagon.

'Will you be able to drive over there all on your own?' she asked, knowing full well that he wouldn't, yet still hoping that he would let her stay at home.

'For once in your life, Christine, would you think about someone other than yourself!' Jack's words were harsh and hurt Christine in a way that she never thought they could. She put her head down to hide the tears that stung her eyes, and stood waiting to help her convalescing husband aboard the wagon.

Thankfully, with one strong arm and one strong leg, Jack managed the feat with relatively little assistance. Christine came around the other side of the wagon and pulled herself clumsily up onto the driver's seat. She knew well enough how to drive a horse, so she released the brake, slapped the reins on the horse's rump, and set the vehicle in motion.

The pair rode in silence for some time, Christine still smarting from Jack's sharp outburst. She struggled to keep the tears at bay, all the time wondering if he was still angry with her, and if he would ever see her as anything more than self-centred. 'Christine!' Jack broke the tension about a mile further on. She cast a sidelong glance in his direction, wanting to indicate that she had heard him, yet somewhat anxious that he was going to continue his reprimand.

'I'm sorry,' he spoke in a much more gentle tone. 'I've been so short-tempered with you lately. I know that you still struggle with fears, and yet I'm so frustrated with myself that I don't seem to have any tolerance for you.'

Christine wanted to ask if he wanted her to leave him, but she couldn't find the courage to voice the question, and besides, she didn't want to leave him any more.

'Will you forgive me?' Jack pressed. 'I really am sorry.'

'Will you forgive me for being so slow?' Christine asked timidly. 'I am taking far longer to gain confidence than you are with your strength.'

'That's not true!' Jack looked full at her. 'You are getting much better. You are so much softer now.'

'Yes, but I'm still afraid of so many things.'

'Like what?' Jack asked, almost sure that he already knew.

'Things.'

'Like my mother and father?' he prodded. 'Are you scared of what they will say to you?'

Christine's countenance crumbled as she nodded her affirmative.

'It's time we set that all to right,' Jack spoke firmly. 'We've all said and done things that have been hurtful, and we've caused damage to ourselves, but I mean to make a start at putting things right.'

'Do you think it will work?' Christine asked, not at all confident. 'I did bring so much trouble to you, Jack. Your mother was quite right in the things she said.'

'We are going to try, Christine.' As he spoke he reached out his previously injured right hand to take her left hand in his. It was an encouraging thing to realise that she actually felt pleased at the simple gesture.

It seemed that Christine's apprehensions were not without foundation as, sadly, Mrs Browning seemed intent upon antagonism.

'I'm glad to see you up and about, son,' Clem commented openly. 'You look well, doesn't he Elizabeth?'

'No thanks to her, I imagine.' Elizabeth's bitterness was palpable, and Christine shrank back at the biting comment.

'We need to talk about this.' Christine could tell that Jack's temper was stirred.

'About what?' Elizabeth snapped, aware of the rising tide of fury, and provoked by it.

'About what has come between us.' Jack tried to sound reasonable.

'She has come between us,' the aggravated mother nodded her head in Christine's direction. 'Selfish, lazy, dirty and careless. And she couldn't even look after my grandchildren.'

The attack was too much for Christine's new state of vulnerability, and she turned from the cabin in shame, breaking into the bright sunshine and looking only for a place to hide.

'I'm sorry, mother,' Jack's tone was tight-lipped and forced. 'Those comments are unnecessary and hurtful both to my wife and myself.'

'Your wife!' Elizabeth retorted. 'When has she ever been a wife to you? She hasn't, has she, son? No, my boy! She has used you to take care of her when no one else would, but she won't be likely ever to give you anything in return. That would be right, wouldn't it?'

'She has nursed me for the last eight weeks, doing the very best she could for me.'

'Which probably wasn't very good, was it, Jack?'

'Elizabeth, I think you are being a little hard on the boy,' Clem interjected half-heartedly. 'I think your mother feels as if Christine Shore hasn't been very honest with you, and that she is playing you for a fool.' Clem directed this comment to Jack.

'There are a lot of things that you two don't know, and I'm not prepared to go into all the details here and now, but suffice to say, I love Christine; she is my wife, and I mean to see that she is treated well. I want to visit with you whenever possible, but unless you can welcome her in your hearts as well as your home, I won't bother coming again either on future occasions, if Christine is not welcome.'

'Jack, don't be ridiculous,' Elizabeth rose up in a panic. 'Of course we want you here. It's just that selfish woman we don't want.'

'It's not what it seems, Mother,' Jack almost resorted to pleading. 'There are things you don't know about. Things that make all the difference in the world, and you need to trust me on it. I'm begging you to forgive Christine and her family. Please don't let your wild ideas cause us to be split from each other for ever. Things are going to be all right. Please forgive her.'

Stony-faced, Elizabeth turned away from her son. She wanted him, but she wasn't sure about letting go of the things she had begun to believe about Christine Shore and her family. Losing her grandchildren had not just hurt her feelings, but had hurt her pride as well, and she had heard a few tales about this woman who forced herself on their son. Tales that spoke of something far less than a decent, godly woman. And Rose Shore, after ignoring the disgraceful behaviour of her daughter, took the two children as if she owned them. She hadn't asked for Elizabeth's help or advice, or even if she would like to visit. The whole situation had galled her terribly.

'If you change your mind, let me know,' Jack offered an ultimatum before leaving his parents' home: 'We will welcome a friendly visit at any time.'

Elizabeth's pride would not let her call her son back, and Clem wasn't willing to prolong the exchange until he knew his wife was ready. He had always felt that there were things he didn't understand, and he never really agreed with his wife's harsh notions. Still, he wanted to wait for her to see it for herself, and so he let Jack go, hoping that reconciliation wouldn't be too long coming.

Jack had a bit of trouble finding Christine, although he found several of his own brothers and sisters, and felt obliged to spend time speaking with each one in turn.

'Mum give Christine an earful, did she?' Jimmy finally asked, when he'd stopped to greet his brother. 'She seemed pretty upset when I saw her.'

'Where did she go?' Jack asked, anxious for his fragile wife.

'It looked like she was setting out for your place. I don't guess you're gonna catch up with that bung leg. I'll help you on the wagon, and drive you until we catch up.'

'Thanks, Jimmy,' Jack sighed dejectedly. 'Does Mum go on about Christine like that all the time?'

'Every time she comes up in conversation. She feels pretty bad about having lost the children, and she reckons it's all her fault.'

'But you don't understand ...'

'I don't need to understand, Jack. I knew something was up the moment you brought Christine back from England. I don't know what happened to her, but whatever it was, it changed her a lot. She hasn't been the same girl I remember from before.'

'It wasn't her fault.'

'It doesn't matter to me, so long as you can live with it,' Jimmy was quick to reassure his brother. 'So long as you think you can be happy, that's all I care about, brother. It's just a relief that you weren't killed in that accident. I don't think I could have stood losing two brothers in the same year.'

'Thanks, Jimmy,' Jack repeated. 'Thank you for believing in me – in us. Christine will be all right, and we will be all right, soon. I promise.'

When the wagon finally overtook Christine, Jimmy quietly jumped down and began the long walk back home.

'I'm sorry, Christine,' Jack tried the gentle approach. 'It's going to take more time than I'd hoped. Please get back in the wagon.'

Christine had stopped walking, but she was hurt and humiliated. She hated the feeling and didn't know if she wanted to be exposed to it again.

'Please,' Jack reiterated.

'It hurts so much, Jack,' Christine turned a sorrowful face towards him. 'I used to admire your mother a lot, and yet she seems to really hate me now. There isn't anything I can do about that. Some of what she says is true, and I can't deny it.'

'I won't make you go there again,' he promised. 'The next time you see my folks will be when they are prepared to reconcile and apologise. Until then, it will be just you and me.'

'But I don't want to be the thing that causes a rift between you and your parents. I know you love and respect them.'

'I love them, yes, but my respect was severely damaged today. I'm afraid they are going to have to apologise.'

'I'm sorry that I've done this to you again, Jack,' Christine murmured as she climbed back on to the high wooden seat. 'Yet again, I've brought you nothing but trouble.'

'Things are going to change soon, Christine, I promise,' Jack said.

CHAPTER 15

C hristine paced nervously about the small kitchen, her worry evident on her face. It had been well over two hours since nightfall, and Jack still had not come home.

The food that she had left in the oven warming had shrivelled into a sorry imitation of what it had been intended to be at the tea hour. But it was not the plate of food going to waste that troubled Christine so much as the fact that her husband had gone out that afternoon on his own, for the first time since the accident, and he had been vague about where he was going.

Now, as his anxious wife watched the long hand of the shelf clock move past the twelve yet again, marking another hour that Jack was late, she was on the verge of panic.

However did I let myself get to this place of caring for him so much that I am about to fall apart at the very thought of losing him, she berated herself quietly. But her imagination would not leave her alone. After all, she had lost Pete and Julianne and then there had been the terrible accident those months ago. It was not that Christine had not had her share of tragedies to deal with.

But could I stand another one? she asked herself. Her stomach was knotted with dread, and she could not even attempt to eat her own meal, which had also shrivelled almost beyond recognition.

It was close to eight o'clock when Christine decided that she could not wait about for her husband's return any longer. Throwing a knitted shawl about her shoulders, she determined that she would walk through the dark countryside calling his name all night, if necessary.

But it wasn't necessary, because Christine had no sooner emerged into the cool night air than she heard the jingle of harness and the sound of an approaching horse. She waited only long enough to ascertain that the vehicle was indeed Jack and not some other member of the family come to deliver bad news.

When she was sure it was her husband who was driving into the yard, waves of relief quickly rolled over her, but then surprisingly turned rapidly into seething anger. She turned from the veranda and marched abruptly back indoors, going immediately to the bedroom where she sat down and waited for her errant husband to come inside.

'Christine!' Jack's tone was light and cheery as he called for her, when he'd finally yarded the horse and come inside. 'Hello!' he called again, wondering why she had not appeared.

When she didn't answer he went in search of her, and found her sitting, stony-faced on the edge of the bed.

'Are you all right?' he asked, somewhat alarmed.

'All right!' she snapped. 'I thought you were dead!'

'I'm fine,' he smiled, brushing her fury aside.

'How can you say that?' she accused. 'How can you just march in here, without so much as an apology, and say, "I'm fine"?'

'But I am fine.' He looked bewildered.

'Well, you may be, but I'm not. Look at the time, Jack Browning. Do you realise how late you are? Do you realise how long I have been waiting for you? Do you realise that I have been worried sick about you?'

She threw all of the questions at him in a barrage of anger, half expecting him to fall to his knees and beg for mercy, but instead, he allowed a wide grin to replace his look of astonishment.

'And why are you laughing?' Christine was not amused. 'What do you think is so funny?'

'You!' Jack relaxed into his state of mirth.

'Me?' Christine looked just as cross as she sounded.

'You're nagging me,' Jack laughed. 'Do you realise, that for the first time in our married life, you are actually nagging me.'

'I'm not!' she defended.

'It sounds like it to me.'

'I'm not nagging you. I'm just plain angry at you.'

'Why? Because you thought I was dead, and when you found out I wasn't, that made you angry?' Jack seemed to think the whole thing was a huge joke.

'Oooh!' Christine got up from the bed and shook herself to ease the pent-up emotion that she felt. Marching past her teasing husband, she went into the kitchen and retrieved the charred evening meal from the oven.

'Since you think it's so funny to leave me here stewing over whether I am to be a widow or not, you can enjoy blackened mutton and vegetables for your tea!' She plonked the plate on the table and whirled about to return to the bedroom.

'Wait a minute!' Jack caught her arm before she could retreat. 'Don't you want to know where I've been?'

Christine didn't answer, having lapsed into a sulk.

'I thought you'd be happy to know that I've been visiting with our children.'

'The babies?' The anger was instantly forgotten, and she turned wide hopeful eyes towards Jack.

'Yes, the babies! And your mother, and sisters.'

'What … how did they … I mean, were they happy to see you?'

'The babies?'

'Yes, and Mum? Was she willing to talk to you, after all this time?'

'First of all, the babies did remember me, and they were happy to see me. I was tickled pink with their reaction. I had thought that they might have forgotten me.'

'And Mum?' Christine was almost afraid to ask

'Well, I had to start out slowly, you understand. I didn't tell you I was going there, in case it didn't work out.'

'But it did work out?' Christine was eager to find out the whole story.

'I had to apologise first, and explain a little about what was behind that dreadful day.'

'How did she take it?'

'She didn't want to know the details, and under the circumstances, I didn't see the need to spell it all out for her.'

'Was she willing to forgive us?' Christine wanted desperately to know the answer to the question that had been foremost in her mind for a number of weeks now.

'She was a little hesitant, but I know that she wants our relationship restored. Those things that we said to each other, the day she was listening, were very hard for her to hear. They were cruel and shocking. It didn't just take her by surprise, but it devastated her opinion of us both.

'I know she wants to believe in us again, but it is going to take a little time for her to trust us. She told me that it was the worst time of her life to realise that someone she had loved so deeply could have sunk to such depths.'

'Oh, I hope she can forgive us,' Christine sounded wistful. 'I want to see the babies so much. I want to see her again too. I want to say "sorry", as well.'

'How does tomorrow sound to you?' Jack smiled at her again.

'Tomorrow! You mean ... ?'

'I've arranged that we'll travel over to the great house and share dinner with your mother and the family there. Will that be all right with you?'

Tears flooded Christine's eyes, and she bit her lip as she nodded her agreement, unwilling to voice an answer.

'And so, am I forgiven for being late in to tea?' he asked with a teasing glint in his eyes.

Christine was more nervous than she had been in a long while, and the fact that they were approaching the Wallace estate was only half the reason. Jack noted her heightened agitation, but instantly assumed that it was her apprehension of meeting with her family after so long a period of broken relationship. But there was more, and only Christine knew the things she had in her own heart.

Jack's bad leg had improved to such an extent that he was quite confident in getting about unassisted now, though he still had a slight limp to remind everyone of the ordeal. He was determined to return to the role of gentleman, and he hastened from the wagon seat in order to assist his wife down, something he had never actually had the privilege of doing, thanks to their strange relationship, and his injuries.

'Thank you, Jack,' Christine gave him a nervous smile, as her feet touched the ground.

'Just a moment.' Jack asked her to wait for him, while he handed the reins of the horse over to Colin's stable hand. 'I want us to walk inside together, if that's all right with you,' Jack took her arm in a protective way. 'I want your mother to know that we are not at war with each other any more.'

'Jack.' Christine halted their approach and turned to him, taking one of his hands in hers as she did so. He looked questioningly at her, though she averted her eyes, too nervous to meet his gaze.

Christine took several deep breaths, as if to gather courage, studying Jack's healed hand as she did so. Just noticing the long, well-shaped fingers, and the large, work-worn hands, seemed to add to the rising emotion that bubbled up inside.

'Are you all right?' Jack asked, a little concerned.

'I just want to say some things to you,' Christine reassured him, rubbing her thumb fondly over the back of his hand. 'Is that all right?'

'Of course,' he smiled.

'Jack, I want you to know how much I appreciate you. How much your love and patience, and kindness has meant to me. If it hadn't been for you, I think I would have been dead by now.' She chanced a look upward, and was caught by the tender look in his eyes. For a long moment, deeper messages of care passed between the two just in the look they shared, and then, Christine dared to move her head close to her husband, inviting him to kiss her.

Jack couldn't believe what he saw, and wasn't sure if he had interpreted the action correctly. She had never allowed him this closeness before, though he had desired it many times.

'Are you sure?' he whispered hoarsely. She nodded her response, and he wasted no more time in capturing her lips with his own. He half expected her to pull away, in her usual frightened manner, but she didn't. Rather, she seemed to melt into him, and he felt her arms go around his neck. He wanted the intimate exchange to go on forever and ever, such was the passion that rose in his heart, but he knew that it was not the time or the place, and eventually he moved back from his wife, more enraptured with her than he had ever been.

'Thank you, my darling Christine. That meant a lot to me.'

'To me too,' she smiled shyly. He grinned at her response, and took her arm, ready to go forward on their original quest.

'There's just one more thing,' Christine interrupted their journey once more. Jack paused and looked expectantly at her again.

'I just thought … that is to say … that when you're feeling strong enough again, I would like you to carry me over the threshold, and we can start our marriage properly.'

Jack was stunned for only a second, and then, as her meaning registered, his face lit up. 'You know, I'm feeling much stronger already,' he laughed, bending and sweeping her off her feet.

Christine giggled like a dizzy schoolgirl, and though she was slightly worried about his recently-healed injuries, she let him carry her over the threshold of the great house.

***

Rose's attention was caught by her two younger daughters laughing at something out the front window.

'What are you girls laughing at?' she asked, curious.

'It's Christine and Jack!' Samantha announced. 'They're here!'

'And that's funny?' Rose was puzzled.

'No! They're kissing!' June couldn't help the silly giggle as she stared with avid interest at her sister and brother-in-law.

'Come away from the window!' Rose was horrified. 'Quickly, girls! I want you over here, this moment!'

'Oh, Mum!' Samantha complained.

'They don't know we're watching,' June pleaded.

'Now!' Rose's voice rose in authority.

The two girls walked crossly away from their source of entertainment. 'I think it's sweet,' Samantha muttered under her breath.

'It's not the sort of thing that you girls need to know about!' Rose admonished. 'I don't know what they could be thinking, in public like that!'

'Why are they coming, anyway?' June asked her mother. 'Jack was only here yesterday.'

'They're just coming to visit,' Rose answered shortly. 'We haven't seen your sister for a long time.'

'I'd say they're coming for more than a visit.' Lady Vera Wallace, who had moved over to the window to get her view of what the girls had been denied, made this statement under her breath. 'This looks like more than a daughter come to visit her mother. I'd say I can see a young man and his wife coming to take their children home from their visit with Grandma.'

CHAPTER 16

Four years later

As Jack approached the manse door he wondered what on earth he was going to say to the minister if he was at home. He'd already lifted the heavy, brass door knocker or he would have followed the urge to turn around and go home again. He felt strangely uneasy as he let the knocker fall with a thud. As his mind went over the last few years, he had a strange sense of déjà vu.

Several years ago he had found himself in this position, standing apprehensively on the doorstep of the manse. It had been much the same motivation then that had caused him to seek the counsel of his friend and minister, John Laslett.

On that previous occasion, it had been over a year since the twins had come back to live with him and his wife, and even now, as Jack remembered, he fondly noted that it also marked the time of their 'honeymoon'. And yet something from the past had still haunted the young married couple.

Christine was so much better than she had been when Jack had first brought her home as his bride, that he had found it difficult then to be actually seeking counsel. It had seemed as if he was being particularly ungrateful, considering the amount of change that had happened, and yet he had not been able to endure the tension any

190

longer. A problem was apparent then, just as it was now, and though he had not been able to put his finger on what that problem might have been, he was not willing to live in silent denial any more.

The situation was the same as it had been those years ago. Jack knew something was threatening their relationship, but he had been unable to get to the bottom of the problem.

'John is over at the church practising his sermon,' Kate informed Jack with a smile, after she'd answered the door. 'Is the family well?' she asked politely.

Jack mumbled an acceptable response, but just his tone told Kate that yet again some ghost of the past had returned to try and steal away the happiness they all yearned for.

She watched him cross the churchyard and knew in her heart that she would eventually be dispatched to offer encouragement and support to Christine Browning.

'He doesn't know what's wrong,' John informed his wife later that evening. She had finally tucked her three children into bed, and was not surprised when her husband brought up the subject of Jack and Christine Browning.

'Well, how does he know that anything is wrong at all?' Kate asked, trying to be logical.

'It's something that comes up every now and then, apparently,' John explained.

'Did you tell him to talk to her about it?' Kate inquired.

'Of course!' John seemed miffed. 'And apparently he has tried to talk to her, but she maintains that nothing is the matter.'

'Then perhaps nothing is!' Kate answered easily. 'Perhaps Jack is feeling insecure about the past.'

'He says that she is withdrawn and melancholy. She goes through times when she won't talk to him, and if he tries to force conversation she becomes upset and emotional.'

'Does he shout at her?'

'Probably! Every man shouts when he's frustrated.'

'That's true!' Kate nodded solemnly.

'I don't shout that much,' John defended.

'Perhaps I don't frustrate you that much,' she answered quickly.

'Let's stay with the case at hand, shall we?' John wanted to laugh, but didn't want to concede to her wit. 'Do you think you could visit with Christine and try to get to the bottom of this ... this tension? Perhaps she will be more open with you, if you promise not to shout.'

Kate smiled at his attempt to get one up on her. 'I'll drive over tomorrow afternoon when the baby goes down for his nap. Annabelle can watch the children. I'm sure she won't mind.'

It was easy to see that Jack had not imagined the 'tension' the moment Kate walked through the door. There had been plenty of times over the past years when Kate had visited with Christine and had found her happy and open. But today, Kate recognised shadows of the crisis they had all endured previously.

'Jack's been worried about you.' Kate decided to come straight to the point. 'I thought he may have been imagining things, but I can see that there is something wrong, isn't there?'

Christine heard her friend's accurate analysis, and while she had pretended and tried to hide her depression from her husband, she knew that Kate would not be satisfied with such a denial. She let out a long, forlorn sigh, and hung her head.

'Is it Jack?' Kate attempted a guess.

'Yes and no!' Christine's shoulders seemed to sag in defeat.

'I thought we had worked through all of that fear and unforgiveness.'

'Oh, it's not that,' Christine hurried to correct her. 'I love Jack. I really do. It's just that, I'm not sure that he really loves me.'

'What are you talking about?' Kate sounded amazed. 'Jack has been like a dog with two tails ever since, well you know, since the children came home.'

'Yes, but that was four years ago, now.'

'But Jack has still seemed happy. You have made a new man of him, Christine. You must know that.'

Christine didn't seem to take the encouragement, despite Kate's best efforts.

'What makes you think that Jack wouldn't love you any more?' Kate asked, determined to bring the problem out into the open.

'He wants a child of his own, Kate!' There. She had blurted it out, and she sat back, as dejected as before, convinced that now the minister's wife would understand everything.

'We know that,' Kate still sounded confused. 'That was what all the fuss was about a couple of years ago, remember?'

'I remember,' Christine nodded, and a lone tear slid down her cheek.

'You told me then that you wanted the same thing.' Kate ventured carefully. 'Has something changed? Are you afraid of having children?'

'Of course not,' Christine lifted her sad face to meet Kate's question. 'I want my own children as much as he does.'

'Are you not ... ? Do you still sleep in separate beds?'

'No! Oh, no!' Christine's face reddened at the implication.

'I don't understand,' Kate sighed, allowing a small amount of her frustration to be expressed in her tone.

'Every month I hope and hope for a child of my own, and every month it's the same.'

Kate heard the confession and saw the large tears that now ran freely down the young woman's face, and she instantly knew what Christine was talking about.

'You said before that it would take time, and to be patient. But I've been patient,' Christine lamented, allowing a sob to escape unchecked.

'Has Jack been saying things to you about it?' Kate asked, concern evident in her tone.

'Not really.' Christine wiped the tears from the corner of her eyes with her handkerchief.

'Then why would you feel he doesn't love you?'

'For years he has talked of children. When he's playing with Pete, especially, he talks about wanting a son of his own. It's like he has been dropping hints. As if I have been holding out on him.'

'But Pete is his son now, isn't he? I understood that Jack had really taken to the twins.'

'Oh, he has, but it's not quite the same as actually having a child that has come from our own marriage.'

'Has he asked you directly about it, or only made references in passing?' Kate wanted to find out the full extent of the situation.

'Only in passing. And each month I hope and pray that I can tell him what he wants to hear.' Her eyes filled up again, and she hung her head low. 'After you talked to me last time I decided to be patient, like you suggested. And I did. Time after time. Trying to hide my disappointment, and trying to pretend that it didn't matter, but I can't do it any more. Sometimes I think God is punishing us.'

'Christine!' Kate was exasperated by the comment. 'For what? What do you suppose God would have in mind that you needed punishment for?'

'I don't know! All those things that happened in the past. All of those selfish things I did. The hurtful words I spoke.'

'God expects you to forgive others, and yet you feel as if He won't forgive you. Does that seem right to you?'

'No! But I don't understand why. Why am I cursed with barrenness?'

'You are probably not cursed with anything of the kind. We just need to trust God.'

'But for how long?' Christine's tone was pleading. 'How long will Jack wait before he gives up?'

'Is that what you think of your husband? Do you think him so fickle that if he doesn't get what he wants he will leave you for someone else? Is that what you think, Christine?' Sadly, Kate realised that she was all but shouting. Frustration was a horrible business, she decided.

When Kate returned to the manse she informed her husband of the day's revelation. 'I guess it doesn't help her knowing that I'm expecting my fourth,' Kate murmured as she ran her hand over her slightly swollen abdomen.

'Fifth,' John corrected, allowing a fleeting thought for the baby boy they had lost several years before. 'I'll have a talk with Jack. I'm sure that patience and understanding will see them through this.'

'You don't suppose that Jack's accident might have something to do with this?' Kate asked, suddenly alarmed at the thought.

'Perhaps! Or perhaps it has something to do with that ordeal in England. And then again, it may have nothing to do with anything of the kind. Perhaps it's just not God's time.'

When Jack heard what the minister had found out, he was hurt and angry all over again. 'Why didn't she tell me?' he asked, his emotion evident.

'Well, I think that you will need to talk to her about that,' John wisely suggested. 'But when you do, I think it would be better for you if you took an understanding approach. Women can become very emotional on this issue, Jack. You could make things a lot worse by losing your temper.'

Jack heard the minister's advice, and knew that he should heed it, but he couldn't help the words that came out of his mouth the moment he was alone with his wife.

'I can't understand why you just didn't talk to me about this rather than going into that sulk. And then you talk to the minister's wife about it. Why not me?'

Christine was cut by his words, and still vulnerable from her disappointment, she immediately retracted further.

'Don't do this to me,' Jack pursued, his ire raised. 'I want to know what you're feeling, and I don't want to find it out by passing messages through the manse.' He could see that she was withdrawing as fast as he was shooting his verbal bullets, and he realised that he should have followed the minister's advice.

'All right. I'm sorry, Christine!' He didn't sound particularly sorry. 'I should calm down before we talk. I know. It's just that I thought we had left behind all of that mistrust and fear. I thought that we loved each other enough to talk about things.'

'I can't talk about it,' Christine's voice was unstable at best, and Jack could see that she was not going to be able to hold back her emotion. 'It hurts so much, Jack.'

Despite his quick temper, Jack could see that he needed to take positive action, and he reached out for his wife, and folded her in a strong embrace. She didn't say anything to him, but allowed the full extent of shattered hopes to be expressed in tears. Jack had a hundred things to say, but he caught himself every time something came to mind, as he recognised his own insensitivity. Gradually, he allowed himself to relax, and he let his own disappointment mingle with hers. Together they shared their grief.

'We talked about this a couple of years ago, Christine,' Jack adopted a reassuring tone. 'I thought we decided that we would just wait.'

'But what if nothing ever happens?' Christine moved back from him and turned distressed eyes towards him. 'It's been over four years, Jack. I'm afraid that there's something wrong with me. Perhaps when I was in England ...'

'Shhh! Don't!' Jack cut her off. 'Don't start thinking about that again. It's over, and we have our own lives here to live. I don't want him destroying what we've fought hard to build.'

'But Jack ...'

'It doesn't matter, Christine. We will wait for God's time, and if it doesn't happen ...'

But he let the sentence trail away unfinished.

Jack had not known about Christine's desire, nor of the constant dashing of hopes that had been occurring every month. If he had known then he would have been able to share with her his own disillusionment.

Just last month, they had been invited to attend the christening of his nephew, and this simple family celebration had opened up areas of longing that he had carefully tried to suppress.

Over recent years he had watched his brothers' and sisters' families increase. Ivy had married, and had quickly produced her first child. Since the time of this nephew's christening until the most recent, Jack and Christine had attended the wedding of Jack's brother, Jimmy, and then his brother, Tom. Both young men had invited their brother and sister-in-law to the christening of their firstborn children.

Then Jack's sister Charlotte had married, and there had been the whisper that she would also be expecting her first child. Each time one of his siblings shared their joy, Jack felt again every inch of yearning and emptiness that his wife had, but the two had not communicated this.

However, none of his siblings' blessings, though they reminded Jack of his own unanswered prayers, had hurt as much as the encounter with his parents.

Elizabeth and Clem Browning had been at the christening service of Ivy's second son. Jack had been cautious of approaching them openly, as they had not given him any reason to trust their reaction. But eventually, out of duty as a son, he went up to them alone.

'Ivy has two boys now,' Elizabeth commented needlessly. 'Jimmy has a fine daughter, and Tom a son. You know Charlotte will have one soon, I suppose. Even your dear departed brother, God rest his soul, has two children, Jack. I wonder what could be wrong in your house?'

Elizabeth's caustic remark had hurt Jack deeply. He had turned from his parents without another word, and he never did share the comment with his wife. But he bore it on the inside.

Now as he held Christine close, he had to admit that it hurt for him too. He didn't understand the ways of God, and he didn't know why it should be that they were left childless when the rest of the family continued to grow.

'Mummy's crying!'

Jack's attention was caught by the sound of his five-year-old's voice. He looked up and saw Julianne following her brother Pete into the room. She glared at Jack as if he should be doing something about her mother's distress. And true to nature, Pete walked straight to Christine and threw childish arms around her. Christine registered his action, and gave a half-sob, half-laugh.

'Thank you, Pete,' she whispered, returning his embrace. 'I am such an ingrate when I have two such wonderful children as you.' She invited Julianne to join in the hug, and Jack smiled as he saw again the healing that these two children brought.

No, he didn't understand God's ways, but he knew that Pete and Julianne were not in his family by accident. God had sent them to be their children. He was sure of that.

CHAPTER 17

Five years later – 1901

'**H**urry up, Dad!' Jack heard the impatience in his ten-year-old son's voice, and concentrated to finish hanging the harness neatly, quickly and on the correct peg on the stable wall.

'I thought you said that you were going to come with us!' Julianne stood watching her father; hands resting irascibly on her child-like hips.

'I am coming, Julianne,' Jack replied. 'You and your brother need to be just a little patient.'

'Well, we've been banished from the house by Grandma Rose, and there isn't nothin' but chores to do right here, so ...'

'So you're anxious to get away,' Jack second-guessed his daughter.

'You did promise us!'

'Yes! I did. And I have every intention of fulfilling that promise, just as soon as I've settled Doctor Michael's horse into the stall.'

'What do we need him for, anyway?' Pete asked, almost annoyed that the doctor had been allowed admittance when they had not.

'Your mother is going to have a baby, Pete. You know that. I don't really want to have to discuss it again.' Jack came away from the stable, brushing imaginary dirt from his hands.

'She didn't need a doctor when we were born, I'll bet,' Julianne muttered under her breath.

'Julianne!' Jack was becoming exasperated with his two children. 'You know that your mother is not really your mother.'

'I know, I know, I know.' She flashed him a teasing grin that made Jack recall a time gone by. Did this little girl know just how much like her real father she looked, and how it struck a tender chord in his heart whenever he saw that smile?

Jack and his two children set off away from the house. In one way, he knew it was best that they get away from what was going on in their small house. Christine had been adamant that Julianne and Pete were too young to know all about the intricacies of childbirth, and for that matter, she didn't really think it was the place for a husband either.

Jack had argued that Doctor Michaels would probably be allowed the privilege, but his arguments fell on deaf ears. After all these years of hoping for a child of their own, Christine was now about to deliver, and Jack was going to do what all good husbands were supposed to do. He was going to keep out of the way until it was all over.

'It's no use you looking at me with those eyes,' Rose Shore had scolded him, just before she'd sent him and the children out.

'But what if there's trouble?' Jack was anxious, and wanted to stay close by, at least.

'There's not going to be any more trouble, Jack Browning. We've had our share of tragedies, and now we are long overdue for some blessing. Now you take those two children out, and you tell them what it is they need to hear.'

The trio set out across the paddock, Julianne and Pete pulling away from their father, their youthful energy and exuberance giving them a speed that Jack had no inclination to match. They knew their destination, and he was not worried about them at all.

They had been out playing in the paddocks on their own plenty of times before, and he would just as willingly have let them go alone again, if it hadn't have been for the promise he'd made, first to his wife, and secondly to them.

They were going to go and visit the graves of their real parents. Ten years was a long time, and most of the pain of having lost his brother and sister-in-law was gone. As for the children, the first Julianne and Pete Browning were only characters in a well-known story. To them, Jack and Christine Browning were the mother and father that they loved dearly.

Jack watched the children get distracted from their course, but he was in no hurry to arrive at the grave site, and so he let them go down to the creek, while he sat down under a tree to watch them splashing about in a pool. He knew that they would want to bring home some tadpoles before the afternoon was over.

It was easy to reflect on the past as his family rested on the verge of a new chapter. His marriage to Christine had started out nothing short of a disaster. They had hurt one another and had misunderstood one another, and Jack knew it was only the grace and love of God that had rescued them from a period of such blackness that death had seemed almost preferable.

Then there had been the time of healing for both of them and the day that Christine had announced that her fears were gone. It had been the beginning of real intimacy between them, but as Jack pondered on it in retrospect, he could see that it had not necessarily meant that all their troubles were over. There was a deeper level of relationship, but that didn't mean that the old fears of the past didn't rise up on occasion to cause tension and anger.

Still, Jack and Christine had faced each obstacle with a sound mind, and each time something came to threaten their relationship, it only took a matter of a few days to settle the issue again, and for them to return to the easy relationship they usually enjoyed.

But two things had persisted over the years. Firstly, no matter how hard Jack had tried, and how hard he had prayed, he had been unable to break through the wall of hardness that his mother had erected against Christine. Jack had pleaded with her, and had pleaded with his father, who, though not in agreement with his wife, seemed to have no influence over her in this matter. Christine had been grieved by the rift in the relationship between mother and son, especially realising that she had been the cause of it.

Even the reverend had tried to get through to Elizabeth Browning, but in the end, he had to admit that it seemed to be a hopeless case. 'At least for the time being,' he had added. 'I have to believe that the Elizabeth Browning I first knew will eventually work past this grudge she seems to have formed,' John said to Jack. 'I have always admired and loved your mother as a generous and caring soul. This thing is most out-of-character for her.'

Jack didn't have to be told this, and neither did Christine. They both knew what it was like to come under the power of unforgiveness, and they both knew just how destructive that power could be. And yet, even with this firsthand knowledge, it didn't give them any more qualification or right to help Elizabeth overcome her wall of unforgiveness.

Jack grieved over the situation as he watched his two children splashing happily in the water hole. Initially Elizabeth had been so adamant that the custody of the two orphans be shared equally between the two families, but since the tumultuous time when Christine had struggled to find hope, and Jack had struggled to find faith, the paternal grandmother had formed a bitterness to which she clung stubbornly.

During the last eight years, though Jack and Christine had worked through much pain and trauma, and the twins had come back to the farm to live with their aunt and uncle, Elizabeth had refused to acknowledge Christine as her daughter-in-law, and had preferred to not see the children at all rather than see them established in such a family.

Many tears had been shed over this unhappy development, but no amount of emotion or prayer had been able to shift this obstacle.

And Christine's own barrenness had not eased any of the aggression in her mother-in-law. Elizabeth had made no secret of her feelings. She had cited everything from the judgement of the Lord, to celibacy, as the reason for her son's disappointed hopes for children. Then, month after month, Christine would cry and grieve at the emptiness she felt at having no children of her own.

At first, Jack had tried to encourage her to be patient, saying that time would bring them their own children. But as months turned into years, even Jack had to admit that he'd lost all hope.

A shriek from Julianne brought Jack's attention back to the two children playing in the creek. Pete had attempted to drop a frog down his sister's back, and she was giving her characteristic display of indignation, fully decorated with shouts of fury and much shaking of her fists.

Jack was amused to see Pete's blasé response. He was not at all perturbed by Julianne's colourful display of anger, and was further rewarded for his teasing by handfuls of slimy mud thrown at his head.

'That's enough!' Jack called out to them, amused and half-wishing that he were still young enough to get away with such a prank. But at twenty-nine, and soon to be a father, he had to admit that it was more in keeping to be the stern authoritarian.

'Didn't you see what he did?' Julianne vented her grievance as she marched up the bank, wiping her muddy hands on her pinafore. 'He tried to drop a frog down my back!'

'I know,' Jack smiled. 'And you tried to throw mud at him. I think you're just about even now, don't you?'

Julianne turned away from her father, a full pout evident on her face.

'Come on,' Jack urged. 'We'd better get along if we're to visit your parents' graves and get home before it gets dark.'

As quickly as the childish storm arose, it abated, and Jack pulled himself up, ready to follow them further up the hill to the family graveyard.

His mind turned back to the earlier thoughts of disappointment at not having children of his own, and he began to think of the time when both he and Christine had realised just how precious these two boisterous children were to them.

'God must have known just how much we needed these two,' Jack had spoken wonderingly on a number of occasions. 'I wouldn't have wished to lose my brother or your sister for anything in the world, but it's just as the reverend has said. We don't often understand the big picture. And we didn't, did we?' he would ask of his wife.

She had acknowledged how grateful she was that in the absence of children of her own, she had her sister's offspring to hold and to nurture.

Then, long after they had ceased to hope for a miracle, the child that they had long desired was conceived, and

Jack shivered with nervous tension again as he realised that a few hours separated him from the arrival of his son or daughter.

'How long ago did our mother and father die?' Julianne asked, staring intrigued at the carved cross marking her mother's resting place.

'Your father died suddenly just a few weeks before you were born, and your mother died the day you were born.' Jack answered mechanically, trying not to think of the grief at that time.

'Did she die because of us?' Pete asked, a slight fear colouring his tone.

'No! Oh no!' Jack moved close to both of the children and placed a hand on each of their shoulders. 'Your mother died of a broken heart, of that I am sure. She loved your father so much, she just couldn't seem to live without him.'

'Is that possible?' Julianne asked sceptically.

'I don't know, honey,' Jack squeezed her shoulder lovingly. 'But none of us can think of any other reason why she shouldn't have lived.'

'Perhaps she didn't want us.' Pete's doubt surfaced again in his comment.

'Pete,' Jack knelt down next to the boy, 'when your father and mother knew that they were expecting a child, they were so happy. I remember clearly thinking that they were being a little over enthusiastic.'

'Don't you like children?' Julianne asked, giving him a pointed look.

'Not back then. I'd just grown out of being a child myself. I hadn't long stopped climbing trees and catching frogs like you. I didn't understand what it's like to want a baby. But I do now!'

'What are we gonna call our baby?' Pete asked, his attention diverted to that subject. 'Will you call him Jack, if it's a boy, or Christine if it's a girl?'

'I don't think so,' Jack answered dreamily.

'Why not?' Julianne demanded. 'We're named after our real mother and father!'

'Yes, but that was because you arrived just as they left us. We all needed to have something to remind us of just how much we loved them.'

'Did you love my father?' Pete asked.

'He was my brother, Pete. I think he was my best friend in the whole world. I loved him very much.'

'Did you miss him, when he died?' Julianne wanted to be included.

'I was very upset,' Jack answered, and strangely, long-forgotten tears brimmed as a testimony to that grief a long time ago. 'I thought my whole world had come to an end.'

'I don't remember him at all.' Julianne sighed and turned away, as if that were an end to it. She stared blankly at the two wooden crosses. 'I know that this is where my real mother and father are buried.' She spoke sadly. 'But I think I have the best mother and father still alive here with me now.' She turned back to Jack and threw her arms about his neck in a childish display of affection. 'I'm glad God gave you to be my daddy,' she whispered in his ear.

Jack returned the hug, choking back a whole range of emotions. Ten years ago, life had dealt a cruel blow to all of them, but now, as time had served as a balm, and as their faith in God had yielded growth and healing, Jack could acknowledge his gratitude to God for the many good things in his life. Even though, those many years past, he had cursed and accused God of many things, Jack was now fully aware of just how blessed he was.

'What's wrong, Daddy?' Julianne asked, panic quite plain on her features.

'I don't know, honey.' Jack was also alarmed at what the three of them had just heard, and he was instantly alert to the many worries that had plagued his night-time dreams.

'You stay here!' he commanded half-heartedly, concentrating on the state of his wife rather than on the two children.

'But it sounds like someone is in pain,' Julianne persisted. She wasn't happy to be put off without knowing everything. 'Is Mum going to die, like my real mother?'

Jack's own anxiety caused him to overlook the fear that the two children were experiencing, and he moved forward towards the small house, determined to get answers to his own questions.

'Come on,' Julianne urged her brother.

'But Dad said we should stay here,' Pete objected without much conviction.

'I'm not gonna stay out here, if Mum is going to die. Come on, I say.' She charged forward after their disappearing father.

Once inside the kitchen, Jack heard the scream of agony again, and he became charged with the energy that comes from fear.

'Rose!' he called, banging on the bedroom door. 'What's going on in there?'

It only took a moment for the stern-faced mother-in-law to open the door and come into the kitchen. 'What are these children doing here?' she asked crossly. 'And what are you doing here?'

Jack had not been aware that he had been followed; even so, it was only a minor concern compared to the anxiety he felt for his wife. 'What about Christine? Is something wrong?'

'Nothing's wrong,' Rose dismissed him, at the same time shooing the children outside.

'But I heard screaming,' he defended himself.

'What did you expect?' Rose was short with him, tired from the long day of tending her daughter's labour. 'Why don't you take the children out, feed the pigs and milk the cow, and by then I should hope it will all be over.'

'So nothing's wrong?' Even as the question was repeated, there were more cries of pain from within, and Jack tensed with apprehension.

'Go outside,' Rose commanded, almost pushing him towards the door. 'Everything is going very well. It won't be long now, I promise.'

Despite the assurances of an experienced midwife, Jack could not relax. He went through the motions of tending to the animals, and even answered the children's wide-eyed questions, though absent-mindedly.

'Do you think she'll die?' Julianne seemed obsessed with the idea.

'Stop it, silly!' Pete thumped his sister on the arm. 'You're upsetting Dad. Just be quiet.'

'But our real mother died, remember,' Julianne insisted. 'Maybe Mum will too.'

The childish chatter did nothing to relieve the expectant father's nerves, and he found himself measuring far too many oats into the horse's trough.

'Dad!' Pete called for his attention. 'You'll give Copper colic if you give him that much.'

Finally, Jack couldn't take the tension of waiting outside, not knowing what was going on, and he left the children in the cow shed as he marched determinedly back inside.

'I've got to see her,' he announced forcefully to Rose the minute he walked in the door.

'Very well!' She stood aside and waved him past. 'And by the way, Jack, congratulations. She's here at last.'

Julianne and Pete peered around the bedroom door, neither one daring to make any noise for fear they would be noticed and chased outside again.

'Isn't she beautiful,' Jack sighed as he held his new daughter close for inspection.

'She looks kind of red and wrinkly to me,' Pete whispered to his sister.

'You've done a wonderful job, my love.' Jack caught Christine's gaze with his own. 'Something so wonderful out of so much pain.'

'Don't mention the word pain to me,' Christine gave a half-smile. 'I'd just like to forget about that for a while.'

The happy couple doted on the new baby for a while longer as the forgotten twins looked on. Eventually, Rose caught sight of the two children and beckoned for them to join her in the kitchen.

'Now you children leave your mother alone for a while,' she admonished.

'Is she going to be all right, Grandma?' Julianne wanted to alleviate all previous fears once and for all.

'She is going to be just fine, and that new little sister of yours as well. But she will need plenty of rest. Do you hear me?'

'Yes, Grandma!' Both of them responded with an obedient nod of the head.

'Now I'm just going to go home for the night,' Rose continued. 'I want to let everyone know about the baby, and then I will come back in the morning. You two make sure you're helpful for your daddy. All right!'

'We will,' Julianne responded for them both. 'Don't worry about us.'

Rose left the house then, and the twins were left to supervise themselves. Their parent's bedroom was almost sacred ground to them, and they didn't dare trespass.

'Who's going to let Grandpa and Grandma Browning know about the baby?' Pete asked out of the blue.

'We could go and tell them,' Julianne suggested.

'It's getting dark outside. Do you think we should?' Pete asked tentatively.

'Of course we should. Dad is busy at the moment, and Mum certainly can't go.'

'Do you know the way?' Pete asked, still waiting to be convinced.

'I know it.' Julianne was quite confident, and had already begun to pull on her boots and coat. 'Come on. Let's go!'

Though the twins knew where their paternal grandparents lived, they had not visited there often. The last time Jack and Christine had taken them was for their Aunt Annabelle's wedding. They sort of understood the tension that existed between their parents and their grandmother, but it didn't stop them from loving their grandfather and the numerous aunts and uncles.

Despite the poor light, Julianne and Pete made their way to the elder Browning's farm, and moved cautiously up the steps, ready to knock on the door.

'What if Grandma Browning answers the door?' Pete asked, somewhat in awe of the older woman.

'Doesn't matter,' Julianne brushed it aside. 'The baby is her granddaughter too. She will want to know, for sure.'

Having knocked firmly and confidently, the pair stood back and waited. Only a few moments passed before the door was opened, and the twins had to squint at the bright light that spilled out from within.

'What is it?' Elizabeth Browning didn't recognise her two grandchildren. She had seen them so little over the years.

'Grandma Browning?' Julianne wasn't quite sure if she had the right person either. 'It's us. Julianne and Pete. May we come in?'

Elizabeth was taken quite by surprise. She had not visited these grandchildren, and she had not ever invited them to come over. The only time she had seen them was from afar at various family occasions. Her pride and bitterness had stolen that familiarity from her, and for a moment, she was overcome with regret.

For just a suspended moment she looked at the mousy brown hair, and the dark eyes of her grand-daughter, and was reminded instantly of her eldest son, *now at rest for over ten years*, she mentally calculated.

'Yes! Come inside,' she answered gruffly, caught in her reverie. 'Clem! The children are here to see you,' she called over her shoulder.

'No! We've come to see you too, Grandma,' Julianne stated with conviction.

'Oh?' Elizabeth was disarmed by the openness of her estranged granddaughter.

'Yes!' Julianne continued. 'We thought you would like to know that we have a new sister.'

'Actually, it's a cousin for us,' Pete corrected, his dark eyes conveying his depth of thoughtfulness. 'Because, you see,' he went on, 'our real mother and father died when we were born. But our mum and dad, who are really our aunt and uncle, have loved us so much that we are really their children now, and so this new baby is going to be like a sister for us.'

'Stop dithering, Pete,' Julianne scolded, in her usual bossy manner, and in a way that brought the deceased daughter-in-law to Elizabeth's mind. 'I'm sure Grandma and Grandpa Browning know all about that.'

'Yes, I do,' Elizabeth confessed, swallowing back unbidden emotion. 'You see, your real father was my son.'

'Our dad is your son too, isn't he?' Julianne asked innocently.

'Yes, he is.' Elizabeth was drawn into this conversation despite her natural inclination to withdraw.

'So our new baby is your new granddaughter. Is that right?'

'I guess that is the case,' she conceded.

'I bet you must be real proud,' Julianne was oblivious to Elizabeth's internal struggle.

'Well, yes. I bet I will be, if I ever see the child.'

'Well, you can come over to visit tomorrow,' Julianne offered without guile. 'I'm sure Mum will be nice and rested by then.'

'Grandma Rose said we were to let her rest,' Pete explained for his sister.

'Yes! But we can make you a cup of tea, just as well,' Julianne hurried on.

'That would be very nice,' Elizabeth found herself going along with the idea.

'We had better be getting along home now,' Pete informed them.

'It's getting quite dark,' Elizabeth sounded concerned. 'Perhaps you would like to stay with us for the night, and then you can come with me when we go to visit with your new sister.'

'Oh! No!' Julianne shook her head. 'Mum and Dad don't even know we have come over. They were so busy with the baby and all. We just thought we would come over and let you know.'

'I see.' Elizabeth sounded disappointed.

'Why don't I drive over and tell your folks that you're going to spend the night with your grandma?' Clem, who'd been listening to the exchange the whole time, offered this suggestion. 'I'm sure they would be happy to let you stay.'

'Well. If you think that would be all right,' Pete looked at his grandfather. 'It would be all right, I suppose.'

'Good!' Clem smiled at the pair with affection, the smile-lines at the corners of his eyes creasing with the delight he felt. 'Have you two had tea yet? I'm sure your grandma would love to make something for you to eat.'

Elizabeth found herself swept along in a rush of exchange, and for once, she didn't try to pull back. Perhaps it was time to welcome change, she thought. Perhaps she should take this opportunity to get to know these two dear children.

'I can't believe those little rascals walked all the way over there, and in the dark too!' Jack expressed his thoughts.

'I'm pleased they came,' Clem ventured carefully. 'That little Julianne has a real way of getting someone's attention.'

Jack let out a laugh, relieving the frown that had been on his face. He knew as well as anybody just how his adopted daughter could worm her way into people's affections, and just how she could wield her strength of mind to get her own way.

'So, you think Mum is happy to have them there?' The frown returned to Jack's forehead as he thought of all the pain that had come as a result of the breakdown of their relationship.

'She seems fine, son,' Clem assured. 'I wasn't sure how it would go at first, but as I say, Julianne seems to know how to win anyone's favour.'

'And Pete?' Jack asked, concerned for his son.

'I'd say he's just doing what his sister wants,' Clem chuckled. 'Does he ever insist on his own way?' he asked as an aside.

'Sometimes,' Jack answered thoughtfully. 'And when he does, he usually gets it too, despite all of his sister's loud tantrums.'

There was a pause as both men seemed to be thinking over the unexpected development.

They both opened their mouth to speak at once.

'Sorry! You go ahead,' Clem offered.

'I was just going to ask if you think Mum will visit us tomorrow?' Jack spoke slowly.

'I haven't felt as much hope of such a thing happening as I do right now. I think you can expect us to bring the twins home tomorrow, and if Christine is up to it, we will look in on that new baby.'

Jack grinned with pleasure at the thought of his new daughter.

'She's a real beauty, Dad,' he offered proudly. 'I never knew just how much I would fall in love with her, the moment she was born.'

Clem gave his son's shoulder an affectionate squeeze. 'Your mother and I have had this privilege twelve times,' he smiled. 'I have a fair idea of what you're talking about, and let me tell you, it doesn't lessen the more you have. In fact, I think we have positively spoiled your youngest sister.'

Just then, Jack heard Christine give a call for him, and he turned anxiously. 'I'm looking forward to seeing you tomorrow.' He suddenly seemed in a hurry to usher his father away, but Clem was not so easily moved.

'Just before I go,' the older man delayed his departure, 'do you think I'd be able to take a look at the little darlin'?'

'Of course,' Christine called out from the bedroom. 'Come in, Dad. Our daughter would love to meet her grandfather.'

'Your mother has insisted that I still have to sleep on the floor,' Jack sounded as if he were sulking, as he came back into the room, after having seen his father to the door.

'Oh, you poor baby,' Christine teased. 'I'll trade places with you, if you like.'

'No!' Jack sounded horrified, and instantly repented of his whining. 'No, you and the baby will stay right where you are.'

'Thank you,' Christine smiled. 'You are a gallant husband.'

Jack smiled back at his wife. 'We've come a long way, Christine,' he spoke thoughtfully. 'Do you remember when I used to sleep in the hay shed?'

'Those were awful times,' Christine turned sober. 'Those were the times when I just wished I could have died. Life was too painful to face.'

'What about now?' Jack asked, searching her face.

'It's as if we were trapped in a cold, dark cave, and now we are free in the open air and sunshine. There is no comparison between what we have now, and what we had then.'

'And now we have this new little ray of sunshine.' Jack ran his work-roughened finger over his daughter's smooth baby cheek.

'Are you ready to name her yet, Jack?' Christine asked softly. 'We can't call her "the baby" for the rest of her life.'

'What name do you think we should have?' Jack asked. 'I mean, there are the family names. Elizabeth, or Rose. Maybe Emily, or Ivy.'

'I want her to have a name of her own. You know, like we discussed before.'

'You liked Victoria, didn't you?' Jack stared lovingly at the tiny infant's sleeping face. 'You know everyone will think we've named her after the Queen,' he commented.

'Yes, but you and I will know that her name tells the story of our life. Victory over the darkness.'

'What about if we call her Victoria Rose?' Jack suggested meaningfully. 'The two names go well together.'

'They do,' Christine agreed. 'However, just when your mother is showing positive signs of reconciliation, I wouldn't want to exclude her in such an obvious way.'

'Then we will call her Victoria Elizabeth Rose. Now that is some name for just a little thing like this.'

'That is quite a name,' Christine nodded. 'And when we have our second, third and fourth children, we will have to do some hard work thinking of names that will mean as much to us as Victoria does.'

'It's just like your grandpa said,' Jack murmured as he kissed the soft, fuzzy head of baby Victoria. 'You are a little darlin'. This day,' Jack shifted his attention to his wife's face, 'marks the beginning of a new era in our family. We have emerged from the shadows of grief, and now we are going to walk in the light of blessing.'

'Amen!' Christine whispered in response. 'Amen to that, for sure!'